Keys to
the Soul

Keys to the Soul

*A WORKBOOK FOR
SELF-DIAGNOSIS USING THE
BACH FLOWERS*

MECHTHILD SCHEFFER

in collaboration with Jeff Anders

translated from the German by Stephen Plumb

SAFFRON WALDEN
THE C.W. DANIEL COMPANY LIMITED

First published in Germany in 1995
under the title *Schlüssel zur Seele*
by Heinrich Hugendubel Verlag, Munich
and revised many times

This English-language edition first published in Great Britain in 1998
by The C.W. Daniel Company Limited
1 Church Path, Saffron Walden
Essex, CB10 1JP, UK

ISBN 0 85207 309 7

Designed by Jim Reader.
Designed and produced in association with Book Production Consultants plc, England
Typeset by Cambridge Photosetting Services, Cambridge, England.
Printed in England by Hillman Printers (Frome), Limited, England.

CONTENTS

Inscription in the old St Paul's Church, Baltimore, dated 1692

Go placidly amid the noise & haste,
& remember what peace there may be in silence.
As far as possible without surrender be on good terms with all persons.
Speak your truth quietly and clearly;
and listen to others, even the dull & ignorant; they too have their story.
Avoid loud & aggressive persons, they are vexations to the spirit.
If you compare yourself with others, you may become vain & bitter;
for always there will be greater & lesser persons than yourself.
Enjoy your achievements as well as your plans.
Keep interested in your own career, however humble;
it is a real possession in the changing fortunes of time.
Exercise caution in your business affairs;
for the world is full of trickery.
But let this not blind you to what virtue there is;
many persons strive for high ideals;
and everywhere life is full of heroism.
Be yourself. Especially, do not feign affection.
Neither be cynical about love;
for in the face of all aridity & disenchantment it is perennial as the grass.
Take kindly the counsel of the years,
gracefully surrendering the things of youth.
Nurture strength of spirit to shield you in sudden misfortune.
But do not distress yourself with imaginings.
Many fears are born of fatigue & loneliness.
Beyond a wholesome discipline, be gentle with yourself.
You are a child of the universe, no less than the trees & stars;
you have a right to be here.
And whether or not it is clear to you,
no doubt the universe is unfolding as it should.
Therefore be at peace with God, whatever you conceive Him to be,
and whatever your labors & aspirations,
in the noisy confusion of life keep peace with your soul.
With all its sham, drudgery & broken dreams,
it is still a beautiful world.
Be careful. Strive to be happy.

ACKNOWLEDGEMENTS

This book came into being during an eventful period in my life, and the manuscript's completion was delayed time and time again by unpredictable – yet still somehow positive – stressful situations.

My thanks go first of all to my staff in Germany, Austria and Switzerland for their wonderful support, understanding and flexible co-operation until the very last moment!

I would also like to thank Jeffe Anders for his inspiration and his tireless involvement in the conception phase of the manuscript.

The section of exercises with the 38 Bach flowers was born out of stimulating team work with Inge Brenner (from Tübingen), Beate Engbrocks, Irina Mamula and Dorothee Struck.

Some of the ideas for Julia Wagner's illustrations came from sketches provided by Verena Baumann from Solothurn.

My thanks go also to Verena Bachmann, Henry Krotoschin and Wolf-Dieter Storl for their stimulation and encouragement.

Lastly, I would like to thank my publishers for their willing co-operation and the organisers of certain publicity events for their understanding when I was unable to meet deadlines at the last moment.

Hamburg, September 1995   *Mechthild Scheffer*

1

A WORD ABOUT THE SPECIFIC
AIMS OF THIS BOOK

Everyone is talking about the Bach flowers currently, and not only because of the convincing results they produce. Many people find that their feelings about the Bach flowers take on an intensely personal nature, some have even declared themselves in love with the flowers. So what lies behind the obvious charisma of this therapy?

I believe on the one hand that this phenomenon comes from the quality of energy – the energy of love which these flowers represent – and on the other hand that Bach flower therapy addresses what may be seen as the most important collective illness syndrome of our time: our loss of emotional and spiritual equilibrium.

At its present stage of development Bach flower therapy has come to enjoy a fairly wide influence. At the same time, it is clear that the possibilities offered by "soul therapy through the flower energy" are far from exhausted, either in respect of the scope of applications or the vast potential for supporting psychic growth processes and work on spiritual consciousness.

As clearly stated in the title of Edward Bach's most important work, *Heal Thyself*, Bach flower therapy sets out to help people to help themselves.

Bach's flowers are still used largely in response to symptoms – to help the soul with everyday challenges rather than help it get started on more focused work on the conscious mind. The latter task is not at all easy without expert assistance, yet there is a great need for it, today more than ever before.

We are often trapped in an unfulfilling living situation or at a stage of development just by certain slight and seemingly insignificant behaviour patterns. Sometimes deciding on just a single positive step in the right direction can be enough. This book may motivate you to take this step, it may provide you with the initial stimulation and assistance or may support you in your ongoing effort.

It is not aimed at psychological therapists or esoteric experts, but rather at the people that Bach himself referred to time and time again – at people like you and me. It is written for those of my contemporaries who have realised that they can no longer carry on in the same way as before and who are prepared to re-orient their lives in small yet consistent steps.

"To forge a link back to our Divine nature", to the positive core of our own being, this was Bach's own therapeutic aim. As can be seen in his later writings, he even regarded his flowers as "tools to be used in the transition period until the time arrives when the original, the immediate are re-established through time or circumstance."

Now, on the threshold of a new millennium and in the process of switching from an information society to a society concerned with awareness, this point could be a lot nearer than many people believe.

1.1 HOW THIS BOOK CAN HELP YOU

This book has arisen out of my experiences in recent years with countless users and friends of Bach flower therapy who have in turn brought with them their own personal experiences.

It carries on from where my earlier book, *Bach Flower Remedies – Theory and Practice*, left off, and as a continuation and expansion of that work it aims above all to fulfil two needs:

- to make the spiritual purpose of Bach flower therapy easily accessible and
- to make self-diagnosis easier.

Many people find it difficult to respond on a personal level to concepts like "Higher Self", "Virtues" or "Disrupting your own life plan" and to integrate these thoughts into their own routine thought processes.

In order to make this process easier, for this book I have taken on board certain elements of archaic models of consciousness. Among other sources of inspiration I was influenced particularly strongly by the Huna teachings – which, to my knowledge, also influenced Bach and his colleagues.

Familiarity with these elements of consciousness should enable you to cultivate more actively than before the garden of your own soul and to hold firm against the widespread "attitude of spiritual consumption" towards Bach flower therapy.

You see, a desire for change is not enough on its own – show me a person who does not entertain this desire – you must make a decision and then act to make that change. You will not be able to do this until you have fully grasped why this change is necessary, or even vital for your very survival.

For this you will need not only insight but also the right information and tools.

Through this book you are provided with the tools in the form of the 38 "Bach flower keys" along with the associated preliminary exercises that will help you to find out how the individual Bach principles manifest themselves in your own personality and assist you in making conscious changes.

These tools should enable you to recognise sooner and more clearly which flowers can help you in a spiritual crisis and how you can quite deliberately plug back into your positive potential again.

This book concentrates on you, not on anyone else. Nonetheless, a deepening awareness of the principles behind the Bach flowers will lead to a growing curiosity to see how these principles unfold in others. But that is a phase that can be left until later, and is beyond the scope of this book.

The exercises are designed to allow you to do them on your own, although you will find some of them easier if you can enlist the help of another person with whom you feel completely at ease. There is no need to go to seminars to learn these exercises. However, if you are currently engaged in psychotherapy you should talk to your therapist before starting even these simple exercises.

I hope you will take the opportunity that this book offers, which is to unlock the hidden potential in your soul.

Become your own "therapist of the soul" with the help of your own consciousness and supported by the unique energies of the Bach flowers, lift yourself out of the mire of unconscious jumbles of feelings by your own bootstraps and get back more and more onto that "path of Truth and Light from which we should never have strayed."

2
THE PHILOSOPHY BEHIND BACH FLOWER THERAPY: EXCERPTS FROM EDWARD BACH'S WRITINGS

Many people reading this book will have already studied Bach's philosophy in his book *Heal Thyself*[1]. Interestingly, Bach is nowadays known mainly as the creator of the 38 Bach flower remedies. His knowledge of spiritual connections and his deep insight into human nature have been pushed somewhat into the background – yet without this knowledge he would never have managed to develop the 38 flower preparations.

As emerges from all of Bach's writings, he was interested above all in people's links back to their divine nature.

There follows a collection of important extracts from *Free Thyself* and *Ye Suffer from Yourselves* as well as from other less well-known writings[2]. We recommend these inspiring texts for your contemplation.

---

1 Published by The C.W. Daniel Company Limited, Saffron Walden, UK.

2 *See The Original Writings of Edward Bach*, published by The C.W. Daniel Company Limited, Saffron Walden, UK.

ALL TRUTH LIES IN OURSELVES

All true knowledge originates within us, growing from the silent communication with our Self.

The dogmatising and civilising influences of thinking have caused us to forget that we already carry all knowledge within ourselves.

We have been persuaded to believe that we need to be taught by others, and our own spiritual Self has thus become forgotten.

The acorn, carried hundreds of miles from its mother-tree, knows without instruction how to become a perfect Oak. The fish of the sea and rivers lay their spawn and swim away. The same with the frog. The serpent lays its eggs in the sand, and goes on its journey; and yet within the acorn, and the spawn, and the eggs is all the knowledge necessary for the young to become as perfect as their parents.

Young swallows can find their way to their winter quarters hundreds of miles away, whilst parent birds are still busy with the second brood.

We need so much to come back to the knowledge that within ourselves lies all truth. To remember that we need seek no advice, no teaching but from within.

THE GIFT OF INDIVIDUALITY

*Has it ever occurred to you that God gave you an individuality? Yet He
certainly did. He gave you a personality of your very own, a treasure to be
kept to your very own self. He gave you a life to lead, which you and only
you should lead: He gave you work to do, which you and only you can do:
He placed you in this world, a Divine being, a child of Himself, to learn
how to become perfect, to gain all knowledge possible, to grow gentle and
kind, and to be a help to others.*

*And has it ever occurred to you how God speaks to you, and tells you of
your own individuality, and of your very own work, of how to steer your
ship true to its own course? He speaks to you through your own real
desires which are the instincts of your Soul. How else could He speak?*

*If we but listen to and obey our own desires, uninfluenced by any other
personality, we shall always be led aright; we shall always be guided, not
only along the path which will lead us to our own advancement and
perfection, but also to make our lives to the uttermost useful and helpful to
others. It is being influenced by the desires of others that takes us from our
own work and wastes our time. Christ would never have fulfilled His
Mission had He listened to the persuasion of his parents, and we should
have lost an army of world-helpers such as Florence Nightingale and a
host of others, had they yielded to the wishes of others and not remained
true to their own heart's desires.*

ON INTERFERENCES AND DISRUPTIONS

It is allowing the interference of other people that stops our listening to the dictates of our soul, and that brings disharmony and disease. The moment the thought of another person enters our minds, it deflects us from our true course.

God gave us each our birthright, an individuality of our very own: He gave us each our own particular work to do, which only we can do: He gave us each our own particular path to follow with which nothing must interfere. Let us see to it that not only do we allow interference, but, and even more important, that we in no way whatsoever interfere with any other single human being. In this lies true health, true service, and the fulfilment of our purpose on earth.

Interferences occur in every life, they are part of the Divine Plan, they are necessary so that we can learn to stand up to them: in fact, we can look upon them as really useful opponents, merely there to help us gain in strength, and realise our Divinity and our invincibility. And we can also know that it is only when we allow them to affect us that they gain in importance and tend to check our progress. It rests entirely with us how quickly we progress: whether we allow interference in our Divine mission; whether we accept the manifestation of interference (called disease) and let it limit and injure our bodies; or whether we, as children of God, use these to establish us the more firmly in our purpose.

Disease, therefore, is the result of interference: interfering with someone else or allowing ourselves to be interfered with.

TO GAIN FREEDOM, GIVE FREEDOM

We must not expect others to do what we want, their ideas are the right ideas for them, and though their pathway may lead in a different direction from ours, the goal at the end of the journey is the same for us all. We do find that it is when we want others to "fall in with our wishes" that we fall out with them.

If we set everybody and everything around us at liberty, we find that in return we are richer in love and possessions than ever we were before, for the love that gives freedom is the great love that binds the closer.

THE RETURN TO INNER EQUILIBRIUM

To find the Herb that will help us we must find the object of our life, what we are striving to do, and also understand the difficulties in our path. The difficulties we call faults or failings, but let us not mind these faults and failings, because they are the very proof to us that we attaining bigger things: our faults should be our encouragements, because they mean that we are aiming high. Let us find for ourselves which of the battles we are particularly fighting, which adversary we are especially trying to overcome, and then take with gratitude and thankfulness that plant which has been sent to help us to victory. We should accept these beautiful Herbs of the fields as a sacrament, as our Creator's Divine gift to aid us in our troubles.

In true healing there is no thought whatever of the disease: it is the mental state, the mental difficulty alone, to be considered: it is where we are going wrong in the Divine Plan that matters. This disharmony with our Spiritual Self may produce a hundred different failings in our bodies (for our bodies after all merely reproduce the condition of our minds), but what matters that? If we put our mind right the body will soon be healed.

THE DIVINE SPARK IN US

Man throughout all the centuries of which we have history has believed that there was something within himself, greater and more wonderful than his body, and which lived on after the grave.

This belief has been in the mind of man from time immemorial.

Every kindly smile, every kindly thought and action; every deed done for love or sympathy or compassion of others proves that there is something greater within us than that we see. That we carry a Spark of the Divine, that within us resides a Vital and Immortal principle.

And the more that Spark of Divinity shines within us, the more our lives radiate Its sympathy, Its compassion and Its love, the more we are beloved by our fellow-men and fingers are pointed at us and the words are said, "There goes a God-like man."

Moreover, the amount of peace, of happiness, of joy, of health and of well-being that comes into our lives depends also on the amount of the Divine Spark which can enter and illuminate our existence.

The link ... It is a very wonderful thought, but it is absolutely true, that certain Herbs, by bringing us solace, bring us closer to our Divinity: and this is shewn again and again in that the sick not only recover from their malady, but in so doing, peace, hope, joy, sympathy and compassion enter into their lives; or if these qualities had been there before, become much increased.

Thus we can truly say that certain Herbs have been placed for us by Divine Means, and the help which they give to us, not only heals our bodies, but brings into our lives, our characters, attributes of our Divinity.

THE SOURCE OF HEALING

It is as though in this vast civilisation of today, a civilisation of great stress and strain, the turmoil has been such that we have become too far parted from the true Source of Healing, our Divinity. Yet our Maker, knowing these things, took compassion upon us, and in His Mercy provided a substitute means to heal our infirmities until when time or circumstance shall restore the genuine and direct.

Yet these substituted means are wonderful in their help: for to see the joy, the happiness, the tenderness that comes into life after life as the Herbs heal them, proves beyond doubt that not the body alone has received blessing.

Moreover, it is certain that it is increased harmony between the Greater Self within and the body without which has effected the cure.

And these Remedies place in the hands of everyone the power to do these things. Not of their own power, but of the Power vested by the Great Creator in His Healing Herbs.

2.1 TERMS USED IN BACH FLOWER THERAPY

You will find the general concepts of Bach flower therapy explained in the greatest depth in Bach's *Heal Thyself*, and a synopsis of the same can be found in: Scheffer, *Bach Flower Therapy* (pp. 15–20).

To help you to work with this book, there follows an even briefer overview of the most important terms used. I feel this to be worthwhile as these terms are used in different ways by the different schools of thought and in different branches of therapy.

THE TWO SPIRITUAL LAWS:
These are the eternal truths that feature – in different formulations – in all the religions of the world. The extent to which people's life plans are realised depends on the extent to which they adhere to these laws.

1. The Law of Inner Guidance
Only follow your inner guidance through your Higher Self and do not allow other personalities to interfere with your own life plan.

2. The Law of Unity
We form a part of a harmonious larger whole just as the cell is a part of the body. All cells are interrelated and interdependent. Everything we do must serve the interests of this larger entity. If we deliberately act against the interests of unity we damage ourselves by cutting ourselves off from it, and we also disrupt the harmony of the whole.

We break this law if, for example, we meddle in the life plan of other people and try to restrict their freedom, if we consciously damage nature or believe ourselves to be above the spiritual laws.

HIGHER SELF:
In Bach therapy sometimes also known as the soul; the divine centre of our being, our immortal true self whose aim is to manifest divine characteristics in the world and to realise our personal life plan. In the words of the bible: *"You should become perfect just as the Lord in heaven is perfect."*

INNER GUIDANCE:
An aspect which is closely linked with the Higher Self and which functions as an intermediary with the personality.

PERSONALITY:
The instrument that the soul uses to manifest its life plan. The personality is the transient part of us, the part of us which we present here on earth, the person made up of flesh and blood who converts the life plan into action.

LIFE PLAN:
The contract for living. It is the map for our journey through life as fixed by the soul.

DIVINE QUALITIES AND POSITIVE BEHAVIOUR PATTERNS:
Examples of divine traits are love, truth, justice, strength, beauty and humour. Our soul would like to realise these traits in order to make the world a richer and more perfect place. Bach also called these traits the "virtues of our human nature."

On the level of personality, these traits manifest themselves as positive energy potentials that express themselves in many different forms, including positive character traits such as willingness, helpfulness and tolerance. These in turn express themselves in behaviour patterns such as behaving co-operatively, considering other people's points of view, showing willingness to learn etc.

FAULTS AND NEGATIVE EMOTIONAL BEHAVIOUR PATTERNS:
If divine traits cannot be realised, cosmic energy becomes blocked. Virtues then turn into faults such as cruelty, egoism, greed and pride. Bach describes these faults as the true causes of illness or "the real primary diseases of man." The positive energy potentials are transformed into their opposites, become distorted and lead to the 38 negative emotional behaviour patterns described by Bach – e.g. to be impatient or resigned, to dominate – which can eventually come to rest in the physical body via the nerve system.

HEALTH AND ILLNESS:
An inner feeling of happiness and bodily health comes about when the life plan is recognised and realised in accordance with Bach's two spiritual laws, as in this situation cosmic energy can flow through the different levels of existence without any blockages or constrictions.

Illness ensues when the personality does not act in harmony with the guidance of the Higher Self, does not take note of its messages, misinterprets or does not want to admit them. Through this disruption of communication with the Higher Self, cosmic energy is distorted, and this results in faults being realised instead of virtues.

THE AIM OF BACH FLOWER THERAPY:
Reharmonisation of the personality; cleansing of the channels of communication to enable the link with the inner guidance to be re-established.

FURTHER DEFINITIONS:

Memory file:
Our internal database, in which everything we experience either knowingly or unknowingly is recorded.

Belief system:
Experience with which we have identified and that has turned into a conviction governing our behaviour, e.g. "Always make sure to leave yourself a way out."

Intuition:
Direct insight. The language in which the Higher Self speaks to us.

Cosmic laws:
The laws in accordance with which the inner order of our creation, the cosmic plan, functions. These laws have been taught for thousands of years by wise men and women, leaders and philosophers from all cultures and in many religions.

Polarity level:
The Thinking Self lives in the world of objects – i.e. the polarity of good and evil, love and hate etc. – and has a tendency to identify with one of these poles. When viewed from the level of the Higher Self, however, the twin poles are merely different manifestations of the same principle. By studying the spiritual or cosmic laws we are able to recognise this and to make a clear choice of which side of the polarity we wish to manifest.

Potential:
Potential in terms of strength or expression.

Projection:
Unconscious personal agendas and conflicts are transferred into the outside world – as, for example, one does battle with one's own father in the guise of one's boss at work.

The Law of Resonance:
One of the cosmic laws.

We resonate with events, people or circumstances in life which match us in terms of vibration – "as above, so below – as within, so without." Each of us can only attract that which matches his or her own vibration at that moment. Thus fear attracts the very thing we are afraid of, while joy attracts the joyous in life.

Transformation:

A major change in a person: restructuring old habit patterns into new constructive ones.

Responsibility:

Taking on responsibility means recognising and acknowledging ourself as the person causing an event or situation, then making a conscious decision and answering for the consequences.

Repression:

Pushing unwanted perceptions out of the current field of consciousness into the subconscious. A refusal to admit to our own feelings and perceptions.

3
THE HIGHER SELF AND THE PERSONALITY

In Bach flower therapy we speak of the *reharmonisation of the personality* – a concept that many of us find difficult to understand. All the same, it is worth gaining a better idea of what it means to allow ourselves to take a more active role in this reharmonisation process.

When Bach says of the effect of his flower essences: "They re-open the channels linking us with our Higher Selves", we cannot help asking ourselves: "How do these channels become blocked and how can I visualise this process in practical terms?" – "How can the personality shut itself off in the first place from the instructions from the Higher Self, and how can I help to prevent this from now on?"

We can take as our initial starting point the fact that no-one intentionally shuts themselves off from the orders of the Higher Self – on the contrary, from childhood on we unconsciously attempt to realise the "divine qualities of our higher nature" – albeit often on the wrong level or using inappropriate means.

Let's take as an example a little girl who would like to make her yearning for beauty come true.

One day this five-year-old girl is with her mother in a boutique when she sees some beautiful, bright chains. Because she likes these chains she takes them and puts them into her little bag. The sales assistant notices this, and the mother scolds her daughter, calling her a thief. The little girl does not understand what is happening to her, and in future will always feel subliminally guilty when she wants to express her natural desire for beauty. So this feeling of guilt will come up later when, as an adult, she feels the desire to buy herself an expensive and colourful dress.

Here is another example: a four-year old boy is unconsciously trying to realise his desire for harmony by trying to act as a mediator between his two arguing parents. This role is naturally beyond his abilities, his efforts are rejected, he fails and withdraws into his inner self in pain. Throughout the rest of his life he may try to avoid conflict in order to preserve his internal idea of harmony in the form of illusory harmony.

Another child subconsciously wishes to realise the principle of **sharing**. On her birthday she takes her birthday presents with her to the kindergarten in order to share her pleasure with her playmates. The other children snatch the presents from her and some of the older children keep them and refuse to give them back. The birthday girl is left empty-handed, and may even be mocked for her "stupidity."

This person will continue to search for a feeling of togetherness, but the search will be accompanied by feelings of irritation or deep disappointment, and on a subconscious level she will probably have the expectation of "being disappointed and in some way always being the stupid one."

In this way, or in similar ways, the "qualities of our divine nature" become distorted in the process of manifest expression. The corresponding negative belief systems then form; the examples above can be recognised as the Bach flower patterns of *Pine*, *Agrimony* and *Willow*.

Negative belief systems are often explained nowadays on a psychological level, but on closer inspection they are always found to be based on a mis-interpretation or a mistake in respect of the two spiritual laws stated by Bach.

In order to address these negative belief systems we have to approach them on the level on which they manifest themselves, namely the psychic level – an approach shared by a great many branches of therapy. We will only achieve lasting change, however, if we include the spiritual level in our measures and if as humans we learn to understand in the most concrete terms possible the deeper and more multi-layered connections lying behind the psychological causes.

With this aim in mind I would like to use the elements of a simple tradition of consciousness that has been used effectively in many different cultures since time immemorial, namely to view the personality as two separate parts or entities pursuing the same goal along with the Higher Self[1].

The greatest advantage of these models of consciousness is that by using them we can recognise quite simply which of the two parts the mental **mis-take or disruption in communication** starts from, and consequently the direction from which the reharmonisation process should be directed. I call these two parts the **Feeling Self** and the **Thinking Self**.

These two parts are viewed as two separate beings in the old traditions, existing, so to speak, in two separate worlds, but having to work together to implement the life plan from a third world, the metaphysical world of the Higher Self. Each part:

- has specific characteristics

- works with specific qualities of energy

- is experienced mainly in a specific part of our body

- has an independent set of goals for development

- plays a specific part in working co-operatively with the Higher Self.

---

1 This concept can be found, for example, in the Celtic tradition and in the Huna teachings. It is interesting to note at this point that the person who worked most closely with Dr Bach, Nora Weeks, was a member of the international *Huna Research Society*.

The two parts also offer different opportunities in their communication with one another and with the Higher Self. These opportunities
can be utilised in a straightforward way for Bach flower therapy.

   You will find on the following pages a summary of the distinctions between the **Feeling Self** and **Thinking Self.**

NOTES ON THE ILLUSTRATIONS OF THE PARTS OF THE PERSONALITY

In this model the Feeling Self and the Thinking Self are the two fundamental parts making up the personality of every human being. However, they are not exactly the same as C.J. Jung's concept of anima/animus.

According to the traditional view, women have greater affinity with the characteristics of the Feeling Self while men can be identified more readily with those of the Thinking Self. In this book, therefore, the Feeling Self is portrayed with feminine and the Thinking Self with masculine attributes.

In your own imagination these two parts may appear differently, perhaps being less gender-specific or even appearing in an abstract form. The Feeling Self might, for example, appear in the form of a circle or ball and the Thinking Self in the form of a triangle.

Depending on the individual's development of awareness the parts will occupy differing amounts of space within a personality, and in the different areas of that personality. Some of you may have a large, powerful Thinking Self and a delicate little Feeling Self, in others the Feeling Self might be huge and the Thinking Self frail and emaciated. After you have read and thoroughly absorbed the following section you might like to draw your own personal version of the Feeling and Thinking Selves.

The illustrations on pages 42 and 62 show the ideal flow of information and communication when the two parts of the personality are acting together in harmony. The golden energy bird symbolises the messenger of the soul, the part forming the link to the Higher Self.

In contrast, the 38 drawings in the section from page 79 to 231 clarify the various deviations from the ideal state of harmony.

3.1 MY FEELING SELF AND MY THINKING SELF

MY FEELING SELF:

Other names: *Younger Self, Subconscious*

lives in the world of "the laws of nature"

- ☞ has access to the "wisdom and power of nature" and can draw on the knowledge from that source

- ☞ as part of "nature at large", of the macrocosm, has direct access to the superconscious, a channel linking it with the Higher Self

works with vital energy

is perceived or felt mainly in the solar plexus region

presides over the physical body and is responsible for the so-called memory file, i.e. the memories of everything that has happened, which are stored as energy in the nerves and muscles

its aim in unfolding: to express itself with pleasure, to be creative, to ground and implement ideas

its needs: recognition in feeling, love

tasks in relation to the Higher Self:
to pick up messages from the Higher Self as a manifestation of the energy of love in order to pass these on to the **Thinking Self**

to maintain and nurture the link with the Higher Self

tasks in relation to my Thinking Self:
consolidating and helping

- ☞ supplying vital energy (for building up a reserve of will-power)

- ☞ storing impulses in the form of energy patterns

- ☞ when requested by the Thinking Self, delivering the stored energy patterns in the form of images and belief systems (chosen at its own discretion), and long-term memory

- ☞ passing on impulses from the Higher Self to the Thinking Self, generally through the right side of the brain.

MY THINKING SELF:

Other names: *Conscious Self, Waking Consciousness*

lives in the polar or dual world of social laws where free will rules

   🔑 has no direct channel of its own to the Higher Self

works with will-power

is perceived in the head: in its harmonious state in both halves of the brain

lives as a guest in the physical body

its aim in unfolding: to bring about accomplishments that will be recognised by other people in the social world

its needs: recognition in society, attainment of wisdom

tasks in relation to my Higher Self:
to accept the impulses sent via the **Feeling Self**
to recognise the life plan and, together with the **Feeling Self**, to implement it consciously
to realise divine wisdom

tasks in relation to my Feeling Self:
decision-making, encouraging and advising

   🔑 initiating contact with the Higher Self

   🔑 organising, assessing and filtering the impulses sent by the Feeling Self, making decisions based on them, and putting the impulse of the will into action

MY FEELING SELF: CHARACTERISTICS:

- responds in a trusting, innocent, uncritical way, "like a child"

- takes everything quite literally

- reacts to stimuli on an image level

- communicates non-verbally, for example by groaning, crying, sneezing, coughing

- cannot differentiate between right and wrong or between external and internal impressions

- maintains contact with other beings on an emotional and telepathic level and suffers in sympathy when it sees others suffering

- being part of the natural world, it is always striving for compensation and balance, wanting to spread harmony

- as the part responsible for conserving strength and regenerating the physical body, it does not like to take risks. It often reacts conservatively (in the positive sense), and has a tendency to form habits

- likes to feel secure and, to a certain extent, guided

- responds to praise and censure, to attestations of authority and will

- can be influenced by rituals and by spoken and written communications from the Thinking Self

- prefers to avoid the unpleasant and the painful and, if forced to make a decision, will do so according to the pleasure/pain principle

- is ceaselessly active, and is happiest working continuously towards a worthwhile goal

- likes to bring things to a conclusion and expects impulses from the Thinking Self to show it the direction or action to take

must learn to become more flexible
not to hurt the feelings of other beings, to develop ever-closer links with the Higher Self, and to let its love flow outwards.

MY THINKING SELF: CHARACTERISTICS:

- ◌ thinks in a linear and logical manner

- ◌ enjoys a command of language

- ◌ identifies itself with social roles

- ◌ produces ideas, thoughts and emotional belief systems

- ◌ visualises in images

- ◌ sets targets and makes decisions constantly, for example:
  to turn to the Feeling Self, to ignore it or decline its offer, to switch
  off or to concentrate

- ◌ can tackle any kind of activity involving thought, such as retreating
  into the past, creating a dream world for itself or dreaming or hyp-
  notising itself into the future

- ◌ can deliberately alter the reaction patterns of the Feeling Self through
  conscious decisions

must learn to co-operate with the Feeling Self, to understand the spiritual
laws, to develop its own capabilities and place them in the service of the
greater whole.

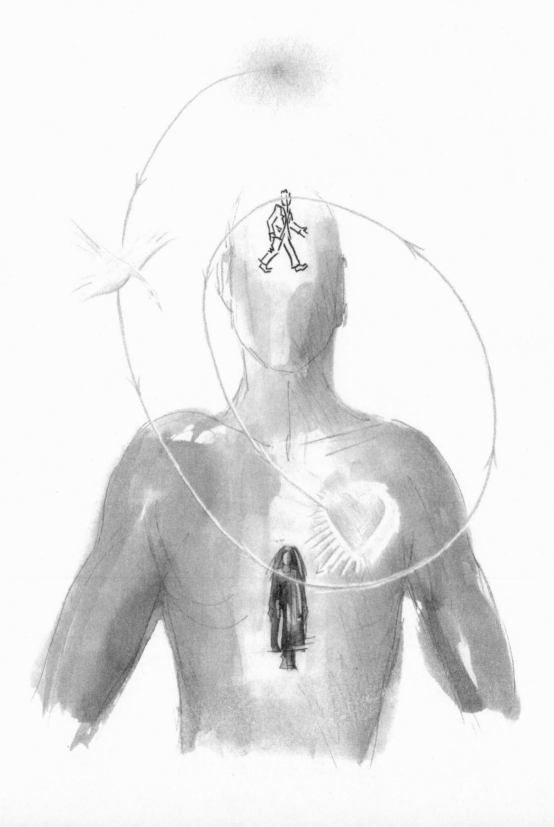

3.2 THE FEELING SELF, THE THINKING SELF AND THE HIGHER SELF

What kind of picture might we have of the **Higher Self** in this model of consciousness? The Higher Self, as the part of us that communicates with the immortal soul, **inhabits a metaphysical, super-conscious world,** in the place where the spiritual laws are laid down and where divine consciousness rules.

It works with the energy of love, the divine virtue of compassion.

It is perceived in our heart, the seat of our awareness of God. Only in our hearts can we truly tell right from wrong. Let us recall here the words of the Little Prince: "*Your only good eye is your heart.*"

It frequently manifests itself, as is often stated, **as a pulsating presence,** analogous to the beating of a heart.

Its aim is to direct the Feeling Self and the Thinking Self in implementing the life plan, and to teach the Thinking Self to think with the heart.

We might imagine that the Higher Self spends its whole time benevolently watching the activities of the Feeling Self and the Thinking Self from a higher vantage point, always ready to lend a hand. However, it does not intervene of its own accord in their activities as that would represent a breach of respect for the free choice of the Thinking Self, and the person would therefore have no chance of development.

In fact, if the Thinking Self is looking for inner guidance it must turn actively to the Higher Self using the energy provided by the Feeling Self. We can find the same law as this in the words of the Christian bible: "*Ask, and it shall be given you; seek, and ye shall find; knock, and it shall be opened unto you.*"

From the level of our limited awareness we can only begin to describe the qualities of the Higher Self. These are said to include divine love and divine wisdom.

Divine love is unconditional love, a lasting affection which is not – as it so often is on the level of the personality – linked with any conditions.

Divine wisdom means the highest form of intelligence that operates creatively – not to be confused with the Thinking Self's intellect on the level of polarity.

3.3 THE OPTIMUM FORM OF COMMUNICATION BETWEEN THE FEELING SELF, THE THINKING SELF AND THE HIGHER SELF

The symbolic illustration on page 42 attempts to clarify this optimum link. The golden soul bird breaks down the barrier between the Higher Self and the personality, acting more or less like a postman, freely delivering messages from the Higher Self if you leave the door to your heart open for it.

The optimum co-operation between these two parts of the personality can be visualised as follows:

The **Higher Self** sends an impulse, a free-form message, which is received unconsciously by my **Feeling Self** and is experienced as a positive feeling such as pleasurable excitement or profound calm. →

The **Feeling Self** passes this impulse to my Thinking Self. →

My **Thinking Self** perceives the impulse as an inner voice, intuition or inspiration – perhaps during a meditation or other creative or devotional activity. →

My **Thinking Self** recognises this impulse as originating from the Higher Self and accepts it gratefully in my heart. It decides to follow this impulse, to realise it. →

My **Thinking Self** knows in my heart that any messages from the Higher Self are in support of my own life plan, and therefore also in harmony with the wider plan of creation. →

The joyous decisiveness of my **Thinking Self** sparks a reaction in my **Feeling Self** in the form of uplifting feelings such as joy and courage, a process which also inspires both of them in their actions. →

The positive emotional experiences that arise from this fortify my **Thinking Self**, enabling it to make further positive decisions in the context of my life plan. →

My **Feeling Self** responds to these positive decisions with yet stronger positive feelings. →

In the course of a chain like this of "God-willed" actions from my **Thinking Self** and positive feeling echoes from my **Feeling Self**, **the positive feeling systems and belief patterns in my Feeling Self's memory have a tendency to become more and more similar to the positive feeling potentials of the Higher Self.**

My **Feeling Self's** memory is transformed.

My **Feeling Self's** antennae increasingly and automatically orient themselves towards the Higher Self.

More and more messages from the Higher Self can flow into my Feeling Self's channels of perception. The Feeling Self and Thinking Self stride ever onwards down the "path of Truth and Light from which we should never have strayed."

This process, which sounds complicated but is not actually so, is described in simple terms in an old adage we remember from our childhood: *"To find happiness in life, help to make others happy because any pleasure we give will come back into our own hearts again."*

Ideal communication between the Thinking and Feeling Selves and the Higher Self is only possible if the following conditions are met:

My **Feeling Self** must have time to receive the messages from the Higher Self and not be too busy or distracted by everyday activities for the **Thinking Self.**

My **Feeling Self's** receptiveness must not be disabled by spiritual or psychological toxins (see p. 57).

My **Thinking Self** must live with a loving attitude toward my **Feeling Self,** willing and grateful to receive from it the impulses from the Higher Self.

My **Thinking Self** must be willing, after checking, to convert these impulses into practical and positive action.

My **Thinking Self** must recognise that the more it turns to my **Feeling Self** and the more positive action it takes in terms of its own life plan, the more "gifts" it will receive in return from the Higher Self through my **Feeling Self.**

In order to gain a more exact understanding of the reasons why this ideal situation is so rare, and how the negative behaviour patterns recognised in Bach flower therapy develop, it is necessary to have a closer look at the possibilities for communication between the **Thinking Self** and the **Feeling Self** and at the factors that can interfere with that communication.

4
COMMUNICATION BETWEEN THE FEELING
SELF AND THE THINKING SELF

4.1 HOW DOES PERCEPTION OCCUR?

In simple terms, the Feeling Self can respond in one of two ways to an impulse it receives from outside, in its environment or from its own physical body:

✍ through a conscious reaction from the **Thinking Self** or

✍ with an automatic reaction from the **Feeling Self**'s memory.

Bach flower therapy strives to encourage the former response. The latter response creates problems.

With a conscious reaction, the Thinking Self consciously detects the impulses sent by the Feeling Self, most positively including the inspiration of the Higher Self.

It tests the current perception realistically, taking into account the images and beliefs supplied from the store of memories and uses these to form a decision appropriate to the situation.

This is sent back to the Feeling Self and is stored by it as a new belief system in place of the previous one.

Example:

Perception: "*There's a smell of burning.*"

The Feeling Self sends the following message: "*The pan in my kitchen is burning. The place will catch fire like that time in my old flat in Munich.*"

The Thinking Self tests the situation from a realistic point of view: *You go into the kitchen, note that all the electric rings are switched off and ascertain that the smell of burning is coming from the neighbours' flat.*

The Thinking Self decides: "*I'm not going to experience a fire in my flat like that time in Munich. I'll ring the neighbours' bell and try to tell them there's a smell of burning.*"

New belief system: "*Not every burning smell that comes to my attention comes from my own flat. If I smell burning I'll start by looking for the cause.*"

By making conscious decisions, the stock of memories – and by extension part of the **Feeling Self** – is subjected to a constant process of transformation. At such moments, and especially when making constructive distinctions, energy is "transformed" and a step forward is made in development. This occurs when we live "in the here and now."

If, for whatever reason, the Thinking Self is unwilling or unable at that moment to pay attention to the perception and to test it, then an **automatic reaction** from the **Feeling Self** will take over.

In such cases the Feeling Self has to take the task over and make decisions alone. It endeavours to do so, even though it is not equipped with tools suitable for the job.

Because it is only capable of reacting it uses the strong memory images that match the present situation most closely, and then reacts in exactly the same way as in the earlier situation; thus the person might lapse into a state of panic and fear.

As negatively-coloured memories are stored with a much stronger energy charge than their positive counterparts, our memory file is quicker to supply negative memories than positive.

My Feeling Self does not want to expose itself to unpleasant memories like these, pushing them instead back into storage, forcing them back "into the shadow." So the Feeling Self makes its decisions by the pleasure principle or according to the strategy "how to avoid unnecessary effort and unpleasantness."

But my Feeling Self cannot get rid of these repressed and rejected impulses once and for all like this. This is because, in accordance with the law of resonance, a stifled impulse begins to resonate again when we witness the same impulse being experienced by another person.

For example: As children we were not allowed to wolf our lunch down too fast, and we now find ourselves in a restaurant sitting opposite a man who is doing just that ... Because this image is associated in our memory file with something we are not allowed to do, in other words an unpleasant feeling, we protect ourselves against this awareness and the mounting sense of unease arising from it.

We can either repress this feeling for an even longer time and move it further from the light of day, where it becomes ever more distorted and "degenerate." Or, we project this one-time ban onto the other person by saying, or at least thinking: "How unseemly it is to bolt your food down like that ..."

In all cases where a perception is not consciously processed by the Thinking Self but can only be responded to by the Feeling Self with a reflex response, the decisions made are not really appropriate to the actual situation, and a constructive transformation of energy becomes impossible.

The energy from each untransformed experience accumulates and gradually crystalises, making the work more difficult and producing an irritation. This is rather like sand in the works, which is shunted to and fro between the Feeling Self and the Thinking Self as the information is processed further.

All repressed or uncompleted actions have a tendency to keep pushing their way back onto the conscious level because the Feeling Self wants to finally bring them to a conclusion and store them away.

The greater this weight, the more energy is tied up in these processes and the more blocked the perception channels linking the Feeling Self to the Higher Self become.

4.2 HOW DO MY FEELING SELF AND THINKING SELF EXPERIENCE THEMSELVES?

As my Feeling Self is unconscious, its self-awareness comes through my Thinking Self.

What my Thinking Self thinks of my Feeling Self, whether my Thinking Self values my Feeling Self, loves it, ignores it or rejects it, my Feeling Self sucks all this up like a sponge. Indeed it becomes that which the Thinking Self thinks of it. If loved it will thrive, if not loved it will become "small and ugly."

My Feeling Self acts like a mirror, reflecting all the thoughts and belief systems of the Thinking Self and answering them with a reaction from its file. It takes each impulse from the Thinking Self and regards it an "order" which it attempts to carry out immediately.

Each time it does this it checks through the memories in the file, which represents a huge task. In return for this task it expects love and recognition from my Thinking Self.

My Feeling Self would also like to be trusted, just as a small child wishes to be trusted by its parents. When overstretched by strong emotional impulses it expects to be protected, guided and consoled in a certain way by the Thinking Self. At the same time it also expects continuous actions of will from the Thinking Self because it needs to have the feeling that it is carrying out a worthwhile task. My Feeling Self is enthusiastic when the Thinking Self also picks up the impulses sent by the Higher Self and they turn these together into action.

The self-image of my Thinking Self is formed from the belief systems and judgements that it has picked up initially through its upbringing and social surroundings, and which it later forms for itself through its own experiences.

Initially, for example, it might believe "I am only moderately talented" as a result of the father's judgement, but later, as a result of its own experience of several exams passed with flying colours it may come to believe "I am more than moderately talented." As a yardstick in this process the Thinking Self uses the criteria of the social world in which it lives – at least until it has achieved through the Feeling Self greater contact with the Higher Self and can also judge according to the spiritual laws.

4.3 HOW MY THINKING SELF TALKS TO MY FEELING SELF

As my **Thinking Self** has at its command consciousness, the ability to make decisions, the power of mental projection and language, it naturally finds it much easier to communicate with the Feeling Self than the other way round.

For this reason the responsibility for good communication with the Feeling Self – and by the same token for communication with the Higher Self – lies firmly with the Thinking Self.

At the very moment when in its blindness my Thinking Self believes that it can elbow my Feeling Self aside ("you haven't got a clue" or "you and your stupid feelings") it forgets that at the end of the day it is completely dependent on the Feeling Self and that in the long run it amounts to "nothing" on its own. From this viewpoint the Feeling Self could be described as its better half.

In what sense is the Thinking Self dependent on the Feeling Self? Without the vital energy of the Feeling Self my Thinking Self does not receive the "juice" it needs to develop the energy required for working or exercising its will.

What's more, the Feeling Self has access to the memory file in the body and thus underpins all of the Thinking Self's activities. Without its link with this file, the Thinking Self has no memory, no facts or material to work with or use in reaching decisions etc.

And most importantly of all: without the Feeling Self's emotional impulses the Thinking Self does not normally have any access to the Higher Self.

In order to maintain a good relationship with my Feeling Self, my Thinking Self needs to learn how to accommodate to the Feeling Self's nature.

Since the Feeling Self can communicate in pictures, my Thinking Self has to convey instructions to it in as clear and pictorial a fashion as possible. It should provide them in such a way that the fantasy and creativity of the Feeling Self are stimulated, so that it gets enthusiastic about carrying out this instruction as a schoolchild does when given an interesting project to work on.

My Thinking Self has to remember that my Feeling Self does not have any intellectual leanings but would like to know quite unequivocally what is to be done step by step and what advantages are to be gained for itself from these activities.

If my Thinking Self does not manage to make it clear to my Feeling Self why something is important to do and what it will gain personally from it, then the Thinking Self will not enjoy any lasting success.

Here is an example that will be familiar to many people – the sorry subject of slimming. My Thinking Self's desire to starve itself into a size 38 to conform to the way we are supposed to look does not hold sway with my Feeling Self. Equally, it cannot relate to an abstract idea of health. The Feeling Self will co-operate with the diet for a while, as long as the Thinking Self forces it with plenty of will-power. But only when my Feeling Self feels physically better, more flexible and better able to express its nature will it be prepared to really co-operate and make the weight loss into a lasting success.

Through its natural link with the Higher Self, the **Feeling Self** has usually a good sense for the true motivation behind a "contract." We can influence our Feeling Self for a short while with noble words and impressive written instructions, e.g. the wording of rules or ritual actions – but sooner or later it will unconsciously see through these to the underlying motivation and, unless it is in agreement, will withdraw from the communication. It reacts in the same way a child does to mixed messages in his or her upbringing.

This is where the great responsibility the Thinking Self holds towards the Feeling Self becomes clear. The Feeling Self reacts ultimately to the level of inner honesty which it senses instinctively from the "tone of the emotion."

Our Feeling Self is receptive to rewards and reacts altogether more con-servatively than the Thinking Self. As it is responsible for our physical sur-vival it is loath to take any risks. These three common refrains sum up its approach: *"We've always done things this way." "Any Tom, Dick or Harry could …" "We've never done things that way."*

So, if my Thinking Self has discovered something new and would like to put a new decision into practice, it must explain it over and over again to the Feeling Self in a sensitive and patient manner rather like the way parents patiently explain facts to their child over and over again. Psychological experience decrees that new things have to be practised at least ten times before an old behaviour pattern can be given up.

My Thinking Self must praise my Feeling Self for any progress it makes and thank it for its painstaking and willing work. We have no better ally in this world than our own Feeling Self. The more we value it, in other words the more we accept and love ourselves, the easier and more automatic is our access to the divine qualities of our Higher Self.

4.4 HOW POOR COMMUNICATION BETWEEN THE THINKING SELF AND THE FEELING SELF LEADS TO NEGATIVE BEHAVIOUR PATTERNS

Behavioural problems on the part of both aspects of the personality are portrayed separately in this section in order to arrive at a better understanding of the way in which the negative behaviour patterns identified in the Bach system develop, and in order to be able to deal with these later in a more focused way. It is apparent that the relationship between these parts is constantly changing and that the problems described below never occur intentionally but rather come into being out of an inner need or immaturity, or through misunderstandings in respect of the spiritual laws.

Indeed, every person does his or her best at all times, that is they do whatever they consider best based on their insights in the here and now.

The main behavioural problems of the Thinking Self towards the Feeling Self

The Thinking Self is not properly aware of its own task and fails to develop, thereby overloading the Feeling Self.

Example: It is not sufficiently on the ball to really analyse the impulses from the Feeling Self and make decisions.

Bach flower pattern: *Chestnut Bud*.

The Thinking Self has an inflated idea of its own importance and tries to force the Feeling Self to comply with the standards of its social world.

Example: It demands that the Feeling Self should understand abstract connections and reacts impatiently when the Feeling Self is unable to supply appropriate information from the memory file quickly enough.

Bach flower state: *Impatiens*.

The Thinking Self has no respect for the inner nature of the Feeling Self because it has not had enough contact with it.

For example, it uses up the Feeling Self's vital reserves without a second thought – in the same way as the human race as part of nature is using up its vital reserves (e.g. felling more and more forests) without any understanding of the consequences.

Bach flower state: *Oak*.

My Thinking Self does not turn to my Feeling Self often enough and neglects it with the result that my Feeling Self attempts to quell its needs for communication, protection and guidance through the Thinking Selves of other people.

Bach flower state: *Heather*.

When this happens, the Feeling Self may be exploited by another Thinking Self.

Bach flower state: *Centaury*.

A description of the Thinking Self's misconception of each separate Bach flower principle can be found on the first double-page spread for the corresponding flower ("flower keys" in the exercises section, pp. 79–231).

Reactions of the Feeling Self to mistakes by the Thinking Self

The Thinking Self can demand an awful lot from the Feeling Self, and the **Feeling Self** will always co-operate up to the point its limits allow it to go. At that point it will revert to passive resistance in self-protection. Thus, for example, as a reaction to prolonged discipline (*Rock-Water* demand), at some time the body will "demand its right" (*Olive*).

If my Thinking Self refuses to take on its decision-making and guiding role, the Feeling Self often starts by over-reacting. It inundates the Thinking Self with emotional impulses – as when a child yells at the top of its voice – in the hope of shaking the Thinking Self awake.

Bach flower state: *Holly*.

If my Thinking Self still fails to co-operate, the Feeling Self can react in a number of very different ways depending on the belief systems it has stored.

It sometimes sabotages the Thinking Self's demands for memories by blocking the file, thus preventing the memory from working properly. It may even provoke a small accident, a sprained wrist for example, in order to avoid having to keep on carrying out the Thinking Self's demands for action.

The less my Thinking Self co-operates with my Feeling Self, the further the two parts will grow apart from one another, and ever more psychic energy will be needed to bridge the gulf which prevents communication between them. The Feeling Self will often, for example, withdraw further and further into its own world, as in the *Clematis* state.

When the Thinking Self is no longer receiving regular impulses through the Feeling Self, it can easily lapse into *Cerato* states and lose its grip.

For the Feeling Self it is very difficult in such situations to maintain the link with the Higher Self as it has to expend too much of its time and energy in bridging the communication gulf.

Although the Feeling Self is essentially always connected to the Higher Self because it naturally belongs to the macrocosm, it is unable to turn directly to the Higher Self for the solution to a specific problem as the conscious initiative must originate from the Thinking Self.

In such cases there is a build-up in the Feeling Self's memory file of more and more unresolved and unfinished business: confused feelings, half-digested negative belief systems, rejected energy impulses which become ever more distorted and turn into "psychotoxins."

In consequence the Feeling Self too must inevitably become more and more distorted in order to stay alive, and this in turn causes its sensory organs to become distorted in relation to messages from the Higher Self.

It becomes increasingly difficult to stay aware of one's own life plan. The

Feeling Self is looking for solutions on the wrong level, is no longer able to distinguish between fraudulent offers and genuine options for solving the problems because its instincts also become less and less reliable as a result of the distortions.

This is why so much emphasis is placed on purification in many spiritual traditions. The Huna tradition, for example, speaks in this respect of Kala cleansing which translates literally as "restoring the light." Bach speaks of the "path of Truth and Light from which we should never have strayed."

Certain people maintain that plants and maybe even the energy of plants have been used in earlier cultures for cleansing the sensory organs of the soul.

For our Feeling Self a thorough bodily cleansing operation is not so important – more important is that it gets the feeling and awareness of "being clean again." Cleansing rituals (ritual washing, confession, ceremonies) in which "the sins are washed away" take on a deeper meaning when viewed from this angle. As soon as the idea of what is clean and what unclean begins to change, energy can start to flow in a positive way.

5
THE EFFECT OF THE BACH FLOWERS – AND HOW THE MIND CAN HELP

5.1 THE BACH FLOWERS AS CATALYSTS FOR GROWTH

In order to be able to work better with the Bach flowers, we should have an idea of the way in which they work, even if this idea – like any such model – does not correspond exactly to the reality.

It may be possible to demonstrate the effect of the Bach flower essences on a scientific level. The science involved concerns the research field of psycho-neuro-immunology. However, describing the flowers from this angle would destroy the terms of reference of this book.

The Bach flowers are often described as "catalysts for growth." A catalyst is capable of altering something else without altering itself, it speeds up a specific process in a specific direction.

As catalysts of growth, the Bach flowers can take certain stagnant situations in the mind and get them moving again through a process of acceleration.

The Bach flower remedies carry information on particular harmonious consciousness potentials from the plant world which match up with corresponding human archetypal reaction patterns. For example, the potential of *Oak* corresponds to the human reaction pattern of endurance.

In order for a Bach flower essence to become an effective catalyst, the corresponding potential on the level of human consciousness must be disharmonious, stagnant, in other words "in need of catalysis." If the corresponding potential in the human consciousness is harmonious, a resonance will occur, but no catalysis. If the corresponding potential is not present, no resonance can take place. This explains why Bach flower remedies that are not needed produce no effect.

Bach speaks of the plants he selected as "die Gefäße aufschließen, die eine größere Einheit zwischen Seele und Körper erlauben" [opening the vessels which permit greater unity between soul and body] or "unsere Kanäle für die Botschaften des spirituellen Selbst öffnen" [opening our channels to messages from the Spiritual Self]. In order to make more sense of these words, let us return to the idea of *psychotoxins*.

If we imagine, on a more esoteric level, a "consciousness circulation system" akin to the various other circulation systems in our bodies (e.g. the digestive and the circulatory systems), then the psychotoxins are the packets of energy that clog this circulation system. By blocking the vessels in this system you would be able to produce inflammations or paralysis of the soul.

Rather in the same way as the indigestible remains of a meal present a problem to the body, psychotoxins are the concentrations in energy form of false belief systems that the soul is unable to digest. For example: "I don't deserve to be alive." Belief systems like this are false because they contradict spiritual laws and eternal truths – the example given contradicts the truth: "Every person deserves to be alive and fulfils a purpose, otherwise he or she would not be alive."

Such poisons of the soul, which are at odds with the law of inner guidance and the law of the greater whole, form blockages and waste in the energy flow that cannot be used for acting positively in terms of our own life plan or the wider plan of creation.

Rather in the same way as harmful foodstuffs eventually affect the blood so badly that it can hardly take up any oxygen any more, these poisons of the soul block up the channels to the Higher Self, causing the capacity for carrying "oxygen of the soul" – the messages from the Higher Self – to drop ever further.

How, in this view of things, can the Bach flowers be seen as catalysts?

On the more esoteric levels psychotoxins act as distortion patterns for energy which lead to destructive reactions like impatience, self-opinionatedness and resignation. Destructive is used here in the sense of counterproductive in the context of the unfolding of our own life plans.

The Bach flowers act as catalysts in 38 specific corridors of the soul. They smooth out 38 destructive patterns of human behaviour, transform them and lead them back to their original harmonious state. The Feeling Self is purified through this process and automatically becomes more receptive to the messages from the Higher Self.

Depending on the level of development in the consciousness of the Thinking Self, its reaction to these catalytic impulses is variable in speed and intensity.

We can work on a wide range of different levels using the Bach flower catalysts – from disharmonious everyday situations to stagnation in the highest levels of spiritual work.

Thus, the Bach flowers are not a substitute for anything else, but they have the effect of bringing about a change in direction by smoothing things out. Energy is then able to flow in precisely the right direction again and the impulses from the inner guidance come back within the reach of the personality.

In summary, we can say today that working with Bach flowers has the following effects:

On the spiritual level: a re-orientation to our own life plan, experienced as a specific form of calm and alert readiness to apply ourselves to life with self-confidence.

On the psychic level: a more conscious processing of experience leads to a more active unfolding of our own aptitudes and talents, and through these an improved grip on life.

On the physical level: the harmonisation of consequences produced by disharmonious use of the two sides of the brain in the autonomic nerve system.

5.2 HOW THE MIND CAN INTENSIFY THE BACH FLOWERS' EFFECT

The negative behaviour patterns identified by Bach arise, as has already been demonstrated, through an imperfect working partnership between the two parts of our personality, whereby the Thinking Self misunderstands the spiritual laws and the Feeling Self makes excessive demands in one direction or another.

This is where we need to start to improve the relationship between the Thinking Self and the Feeling Self in specific areas. The initiative for this can only come from the Thinking Self.

Not until your Thinking Self has totally convinced your Feeling Self that the negative self-perceptions (e.g. false feelings of guilt, low self-esteem etc.) are out of line with the inner truth will it be ready to give up these misconceptions or illusions – like simply throwing away an out-of-date timetable.

When both parts have inwardly absorbed the fact that they are created from divine matter – and are therefore essentially incapable of being bad – and are both looking forward together to starting a new, positive life, there is a good chance of tapping into the huge source of power that is now still lying dormant and blocked off within you. In this spiritual climate the selected positive impulses of the Bach flowers can come into contact with deeper layers of your true being. Why not take that first, decisive step now?

Make a fundamental decision that from now on you intend to turn unreservedly to your Feeling Self – and therefore also to your Higher Self.

"Unreservedly" means not now and then, but all the time.

There are many ways to make progress in this sometimes difficult process. Here is a suggestion based on the Bach principle of simplicity: for a limited period of a few weeks or more try consciously holding back 90% of your outward-directed feelings for other people, turning this energy instead towards your own Feeling Self.

Make your Feeling Self your closest confidante, which is in any case its natural role!

Modify the adage quoted on page 45 to read as follows:
"If you want to be happy in life, help make your Feeling Self happy,
because the joy we give to the Feeling Self
returns as an echo from the Higher Self, as love and wisdom
into your own heart."

Mind you, this recommendation is not intended to put you into the self-centred *Heather* state nor cause you to become an egoist. It is a short-term self-therapeutic technique, and you should make certain preparations in the world around you before using it.

At first glance this suggestion may also appear to many people as rather un-Christian, yet in our Christian past we often failed to ask the question of whether we can give what we do not ourselves possess. How can we approach another person with a positive feeling when we have not accepted ourselves and have no idea "what a positive feeling actually feels like."

Turning our attention to our own Feeling Selves leads to improved contact with our own Higher Self.

And the more of the Higher Self's directives we can integrate into our lives, the more positive contribution we make quite automatically to the happiness of others and to the greater whole.

Another suggestion for making the most of the energy of the Bach flowers:

Make each time that you take your Bach flower remedy into a "mini-ritual."

Link your Thinking Self with your Feeling Self through "conscious breathing" and say either to yourself or out loud the intention you want to support by taking the remedy, for example, "I come to recognise more and more clearly ..." As the Feeling Self normally presides over breathing as a bodily function, it will turn immediately to the Thinking Self if the latter takes over its job.

At the same time in the process you transpose the vital energy of the Feeling Self to the higher level of energy of the will. This has the effect of making a stronger impression on the Feeling Self, which then feels more involved in an important process. At this moment the two parts are working totally in unison with one another.

With your Thinking Self, take up the impulses of the Bach flowers and work more on them in a focused way – for example in a diary or any other form of awareness work.

The deeper the level on which you can understand the lessons taught by the individual Bach flowers and their relevance to your own life, the more benefit you will gain from them. The exercises in the next section are designed to provide a simple introduction to this process.

6

INTRODUCTION TO WORKING WITH THE 38 BACH FLOWER PRINCIPLES

6.1 IN PREPARATION ...

Before you embark on your 38-day course – the recommended duration – to arrive at a personal interpretation of the Bach concepts, to help you into the right frame of mind I include here as a quotation some words Edward Bach delivered to his colleagues in the form of an appeal:

"The greatest gift we can make to our fellow human beings is to be balanced and happy in ourselves. In this way we can lift them up out of their depression."

Overcoming negative attitudes in our own souls is a "deadly serious" matter as it is essential for life, yet it is even more important to approach this task in a playful and cheerful manner. If your Feeling Self will not play along with this, you can forget any idea of a positive outcome. In other words: make sure that you enjoy this little self-initiation into the world of Bach flower concepts and that you are looking forward to the task ahead.

What materials do you need for this work? You probably already have everything you need at home: a timer, a firm portable writing surface (e.g. clipboard), a CD player or a cassette recorder, sheets of yellow and white paper or index cards and, although not absolutely essential, a set of original English Bach flower concentrates. Lastly, you should have some large notebooks or a ring binder to use as a flowers journal.

The following repertoire of exercises is a suggestion which you can either follow through as described or adapt to suit your individual preferences.

Although a lot of self-therapeutic effects are intended to occur in the course of the exercises, we cannot expect a problem to be completely solved through performing an exercise just once. The exercises should simply indicate where the lever should be applied in order to overcome a negative Bach flower state, and what kind of further mental work is required either on your own or, in certain cases, with the support of a professional.

The responsibility for carrying out these exercises lies entirely with you, but we can offer you one or two tips to get you started.

Never work with more than one flower on any one day. If possible, you should even allow yourself longer, perhaps a weekend or a whole week.

Maintain a playful lightness, don't allow yourself to get too worked up about the exercises and avoid overdoing it.

If any of the exercises disturbs your spiritual equilibrium you must restore it through a centring exercise (see Section 6.2). If necessary, you should abandon the exercise and try it again on the following day, if possible with a friend to accompany you.

Rescue remedy, the emergency combination – which could be taken in situations like this – is not included in the programme of exercises as it does not stand for any individual principle, but balances out a combination of states. You will work on the individual principles contained in *Rescue* remedy in the corresponding exercise sections.

For the exercises you can, if you wish, also take two drops of the corresponding Bach flowers in a glass of water. You should, however, be aware that the flowers' energy can move blockages in the subconscious which would then really need to be worked on further.

You are always recommended to take the remedy if you discover yourself to be in an acute negative state of the flower principle in question.

When taking a remedy, start by breathing in deeply, then drink a mouthful from the glass while either imagining or saying out loud what you hope to achieve with the help of the flowers' energy.

It's up to you whether you prefer to work with or without the support of the flowers themselves. It may even be interesting to carry out an exercise once with support from the Bach flower, and then repeat it a few days later without taking the flower.

You can, of course, start with the first flower and work through them in sequence from 1 to 38. It is more advisable, however, to choose a flower to suit the mood or the "quality of time" that day. Select the flower you wish to work with through a centring exercise or ask your Feeling Self what it would like to explore on a particular day.

All the exercises start in the same way: with centring.

Notes on centring and on communication with our inner guidance can be found in the next section, working with the flowers journal is described in Section 6.4, and supplementary notes and first-hand accounts of experiences can be found in Section 6.5.

6.2 HOW DO I ESTABLISH A LINK WITH MY HIGHER SELF?

We might have gained a theoretical understanding of the idea that our true inner nature is the Higher Self, but many of us are not yet able to really visualise this, as we identify ourselves so strongly with the thoughts, feelings and perceptions that we take in from the outside world.

Contacting the **Higher Self** is easily said but not so easily done. For most people it is a lengthy process with a great many intermediate stages.

We occasionally use the term *inner guidance* in this book to avoid giving the false impression that we can reach our Higher Self automatically through making a new decision or modifying an intention.

The Thinking Self needs to consciously strive for a relationship with the Higher Self, and that relationship needs to be cultivated by the Feeling Self. For this we need sensitivity, courage and will.

Connecting back to the Higher Self

Setting ourselves the target of reaching the Higher Self does not, however, mean the same as becoming the Higher Self, but rather giving expression to the divine qualities of the Higher Self on the levels of the Feeling Self and the Thinking Self. That means that everything we do must always take into account the requirements of all three levels, otherwise only a partial plan will be realised rather than the complete life plan.

It becomes clear from this that we can only follow our inner guidance when we switch on our Thinking Self and develop ever-greater awareness. If we try to reach our Higher Self through our Feeling Self alone, which lacks the ability to differentiate, we can easily come to regard distorted or illusory beliefs from the Feeling Self's store as genuine messages from the Higher Self, and thus go astray – as happens time and time again in the tragic development of certain sects.

An awareness that originates from the Higher Self always contains aspects of a deep inner calm, safety and security.

It is equally important that we should avoid confusing or mixing up the ideals and laws of the different levels. For example, if the Feeling Self, which includes the body, finds itself in danger, we must fight actively to enable it to survive and we cannot expect the Higher Self to deal with it. That being so, at times like this we should still ask the Higher Self for appropriate insights and ideas.

In order to find the right way to establish contact with the Higher Self, we must constantly remember that the behaviour and qualities of the Higher Self are very different from those of the Thinking Self, every bit as different as is the Thinking Self's level of consciousness from that of the Feeling Self.

The best idea is to meet the Higher Self with an attitude of openness and impartial curiosity, rather like when we meet a new person on a social level and become aware of a desire to get to know him or her better.

We may not confront the Higher Self with demands or arrive at excessively fixed ideas of the type and contents of its messages, neither may we attempt to "force it down" onto the level of the Thinking Self.

Our life plan, which the Higher Self knows best of all, may have a very different shape from that which we believe it has at the moment. We should be ready for surprises.

The first step: centring

Any technique or path that helps us to centre ourselves and to subdue the thoughts, feelings and perceptions that divert our attention is able to take us on the first step of this journey. In this way we learn not to allow our attention to be distracted by the impulses from the inner guidance that our Higher Self is constantly trying to impart to us.

Novices to the area of centring will be keen to find the answer to the question: "*How can I be sure that I am not centred?*"

Any of the 38 negative Bach flower states – in other words any feeling that is not comfortable – may signal the fact that we are not sufficiently centred.

This state is often described as being "not fully awake, as in a trance, not having one's feet on the ground, not being all there", but also as "feeling uncomfortable in one's body, feeling inwardly flattened or uncertain."

There are other factors apart from spiritual reasons or physical traumas that can knock us off-centre. The wrong types of food, an excess of stimulants, not enough sleep, becoming too cold or too hot can all also prevent the various levels of the bioenergetic field from working together in harmony. So, when we are in a centred state we often experience a gentle and automatic process of "circling around ourselves", through which the various bioenergetic levels are balancing themselves out again.

What does centring mean, and what are the different ways of going about it?
Instead of centring we could speak of meditating, grounding ourselves or contemplation – no matter which word we use, in the final analysis it means consciously directing all our attention inward in order to gain a sense that we have found our true inner selves, arrived at a place where we feel stable and secure, where we have made contact with ourselves.

In this state of keen concentration, in which we often lose our normal sense of time and a feeling of timelessness comes in, the channels leading to our inner guidance are opened and we are frequently able to perceive the impulses from the Higher Self as inspiration.

But the meditative approach is not the only way we can centre ourselves; we can also do it through the body by breathing, through yoga, dancing and t'ai chi as well as through creative activities like potting, painting or singing. Some people even centre themselves through activities like tidying up their garden shed or making a list of things to buy for a party.

The hallmark of centring is that it involves no stressful mental activity, it should be effortless and we should find it pleasurable. When we are centred we have the feeling of being at the centre of our selves, of being fully alert. We feel calm and strong in a gentle way and we have the inner certainty of possessing courage through which we can act at any time.

For many people, centred also means being in harmony with themselves and with the world. In this state we are in a position to watch the daily dealings between the Thinking Self and the Feeling Self from a higher vantage point so that the impulses from the inner guidance can make themselves felt in us.

Edward Bach recommended a simple form of centring that anyone can perform in any situation: to sit down quietly in peaceful surroundings for 15 minutes at the same time every day and reflect on the experiences of the day and of our lives.

Qualities of the Higher Self which we can often become aware of when in a centred state

We feel alive, confident, objective, clear, calm, secure, knowing, brave, accepting, sympathetic, understanding, unshackled etc.

Your personal path to your centre

It is important to find your own path which enables you to draw back to your centre at any time, and to develop an awareness of the difference between this inner place in yourself and normal, everyday consciousness. With time you will learn to move consciously backwards and forwards between these two places.

Many people reading this book will have found their own personal way of centring themselves long ago. For those who have not yet experienced centring consciously in this way, there are countless different ways of becoming familiar with the feeling. If you are intending to work on this, you should now be able to find the approach that suits you best.

Centring yourself before the exercises

You can perform this centring exercise when starting to work with the individual flowers: Read the key page for the flower you intend working with (see Section 6.3). Get into your centred state and then ask your inner guidance to let anything come up in you which is important for you personally in relation to this flower concept.

If you wish, you could write down in your Bach flowers journal either immediately or later everything that occurs to you.

If one idea surfaces and then leads on to another, you should go along with them. Don't try to control these perceptions but simply follow the flow of your impressions.

This exercise is meant to allow unconscious personal memories to come to the surface. If you notice that the flow from inside you is drying up, you should stop, breathe deeply and finish the exercise.

It is always advisable to perform this exercise in conjunction with Exercise 3 from the sections on the individual flowers.

6.3 GUIDE TO THE EXERCISES SECTION

The exercises in this book have been designed to help you to become more aware of your own personal experience of each flower principle.

Each Bach flower principle is given two double pages

First double page: The flower key
At the top of the page you will find a brief description showing the primary characteristics of the Bach flower in question. The direction of the flower's harmonising effect is also shown.
For example:

FROM SELF-RESTRICTION ... TO SELF-UNFOLDING ...

19. LARCH
THE SELF-TRUST FLOWER

This is the theme, the message of this flower in a nutshell. It only contains the most important facet of the flower rather than all its possible facets as the flower principle is ultimately experienced differently by each individual.

The flower key should explain the flower to your Thinking Self.

So, for example, you learn:

1. How can I tell when I am in the negative *Larch* state?

This paragraph illustrates by example the thoughts, feelings and reactions by which you can recognise the negative flower state in question. Find your own examples for each flower.

2. How does the disruption of communication with my inner guidance come about?

This paragraph explains how the Thinking Self and the Feeling Self have disengaged themselves from the Higher Self, and which of the two parts of the personality is more responsible for this specific disruption of equilibrium.

Here, either the Thinking Self can become too independent and disengage itself from the Feeling Self, or the Feeling Self can feel abandoned by the Thinking Self and react in a destructive way. Or, the Thinking Self and Feeling Self share the blame for getting themselves in a tangle and losing contact with the Higher Self, and are stubbornly maintaining an illusory world of thoughts and feelings on the level of polarity.

This is also shown through the illustration at the bottom of the right-hand page: it shows whether and how the golden "soul bird", carrier of impulses from the Higher Self, is still connected with the personality, and whether the personality still has access to the cosmic energy source. The part of the personality from which the disruption originates can be seen on the right of each illustration.

3. Which mental truth does my Thinking Self either ignore or misunderstand?

This paragraph sets out to clarify how the misunderstanding in the mind and the distortion have come about, where the Thinking Self is acting in good faith but under a misconception, or how it can get confused between the different levels.

4. Which conscious decision or intention will link me with my inner guidance again?

In order to stimulate thought, this paragraph presents a possible decision for the necessary change in direction. You should arrive at your own formulation through your work with each flower concept.

5. Which qualities will help me here?

Various positive qualities or virtues are listed here which will help you to implement your decision. It is worthwhile developing these virtues!

6. How can I tell when my positive ... potential is growing?

Through example the terms of reference are set down here explaining how we will feel if we develop the positive potential of the flower more and more. You should also develop your own formulations in this area in the course of your work.

Second double page: Deeper exercises on the flower principle

The second double page is the work page which you can use to develop the flower potential for yourself.

The flower image

We have consciously avoided illustrating the physical form of the flower here, instead we have attempted to explore visually the flower's principle.

The flower images appear at the top on the left-hand page, and with their mandala-like structure they lend themselves for use as a centring aid for immersion in the flower principle concerned.

Botanists have been using flower images to characterise plant families according to their specific features since the second half of the 19th century.

So "plant outlines" have developed, in which the individual parts of a flower are arranged spatially and projected onto a flat surface.

Some readers may feel moved to colour the images according to their own personal feelings in the course of their work with the flower principles.

Needless to say, focusing on a flower image can never take the place of encountering a living plant in the natural world.

If you have the opportunity you should find and learn the Bach flowers as they grow wild in the natural world, get in tune with the energy that emanates from them, and become more and more receptive to them. We would urge you strongly to try this kind of meditation or concentration in the presence of a living plant in the natural world.

The flower exercises

These exercises deliberately bring the flower principle onto an apparently banal everyday level, the level on which it manifests itself, where we have to live it – indeed the level where the result of its conscious transformation will finally be seen. The exercises are aimed partly at your Feeling Self and partly at your Thinking Self.

Exercise 1: Experience the negative flower state as consciously as possible:

This exercise is designed to help readers who have little prior experience of the flower state in question to place themselves into that state either directly or on a symbolic level. If you are already perfectly familiar with the principle in question you may skip this exercise.

Exercise 2: Observe the flower principle around you:

In the second exercise we want to develop an awareness of the Bach principle in question as an observer, as we experience it in our daily lives. To save space, only a few examples are outlined. In the column "Supplementary personal notes" you can note down your own examples – particularly for the positive side of the principle.

Exercise 3: Discover and develop your positive flower potential:

The third exercise builds a bridge that helps you to cross smoothly over from the negative to the positive potential of the principle. These exercises are also deliberately kept simple, and you can work through the questions with members of your family or even children.

By way of explanation we have chosen as examples common everyday psychological situations. For each flower you should find an up-to-date example that is important to you personally in relation to this flower concept.

However, we would advise you not to try solving any serious or complex problems in this way. Start with something simple and see how the principle works.

If you want to tackle more complex problems in this way, you should later work out for yourself a personal combination of Bach flower exercises.

It is advisable to repeat the centring exercise at the end of a sequence of exercises, asking yourself the following questions:

"What will I gain if I decide to actually put the experience from the exercise into action?"

"Which of my untapped positive qualities will then finally be able to unfold?"

It might even be fun to discuss these questions inwardly with your Thinking Self and your Feeling Self.

The "flower strip"

To conclude your work with the flower concept you will find at the bottom of the page a strip with 12 circles for marking with crosses. The idea of this is to enable you to keep track of and to evaluate the results of your work.

The numbers 1 to 12 stand for specific questions which you will find in Section 8.1.

When you have reached the end of your work with all the Bach flower essences and have transferred the details from the flower bars, you can then create your personal flower profile (see Section 8.1).

6.4 THE BACH FLOWERS JOURNAL

Buy yourself an A4 notebook or a diary with a nice cover according to your personal taste, or an A4 ring binder so that you can move the pages around and add to them. This is your Bach flowers journal, in which you can collect and document the fruits of your own work with the Bach flower principles. In this journal you keep a record of your experiences with the exercises, writing down which personal examples you have worked on and the results you were able to achieve.

The aim is to find out what the positive potential means to you personally.

> E.g.: *"Mimulus-bravery for me is opening letters from Dr X without my heart pounding."*

Recognise the contribution made to your personal development by working with the particular flower concept.

> E.g.: *"It enabled me to get things out in the open with my father, which was long overdue."*

The most important thing is to keep a handle on how you want to bring about a positive change of direction with respect to the principle concerned.

> E.g. for Gentian: *"I'm not going to join in any more when other people start talking pessimistically about the future of our city."*

If you feel like it you could also draw, paint or glue the Bach flower in your journal and sketch your Thinking and Feeling Selves. You might also come across interesting sayings, cartoons, music titles or characters from film, television or books which embody the principle for you – or a small object, a gesture, word or sound that symbolises the principle for you.

If you would like you can set up two diaries from the very start: the first only for the 38 days of exercises and the second for additional experiences. You can keep adding to the latter as you collect flower experiences for this concept relating to members of your family, friends, colleagues etc.

During this work you should take note of ways in which the positive potentials are increasingly becoming an integral part of your personality and your life. After a few months or years you will have an invaluable personal Bach flowers database.

If you find that you have slipped back into the negative state, you can work out where your personal "connecting switch", your bridge to your own positive potential is to be found. Your flowers journal documents your own path for reaching your positive potential quickly again.

For example: *"If I find myself back in the Gentian state I think of the optimistic Mr Jones."*

To give you some ideas, on the next page you will find an example of how such a flowers journal page can be structured.

My experiences with the Gentian potential   Date:...

Which examples did I use for the exercises?

Where did I recognise *Gentian* in the world around me?

How intensive was my experience with the flower exercises?...

Very strong	Medium	Weak

How good was my grasp of the *Gentian* principle?...

Very good	Good	Moderate

Would I like to do further work on this principle?

Yes	No	Later

My most important experience of *Gentian:*

E.g.: *"When I am in the Gentian state I repeat my mother's behaviour."*

Negative *Gentian* potential is for me:

"Doubting that anything will come of a planned project."

In which area of my life is the *Gentian* principle especially important (work, private life, spiritual development etc.)?

"In my private life, in my relationship with my mother."

The positive quality of *Gentian* is for me:

"Having confidence that a planned project will turn out to be a success."

My bridge to the positive *Gentian* potential is:

"I see in front of my eyes and feel once again the happiness when as a little girl I won the hurdles at the school sports day despite doubting myself before the race."

This point should enable you in due course to make a conscious connection to your positive potential for the flower, even without taking the drops.

Where did I realise the positive Gentian potential today?

"In the coffee break I didn't enter into my colleagues' pessimistic discussions."

Which positive *Gentian* activity will I undertake in the next 3 days?

"I will telephone my gloomy aunt and give her some encouragement."

When:

(Enter date when done)

6.5 SUPPLEMENTARY NOTES AND EXPERIENCES WITH THE BACH FLOWER EXERCISES

Every day is different

When you do the Bach flower exercises you will notice that every day you are in a different state of mind, a different mood. Our perception – how we experience ourselves, everyday situations or a flower principle – is likewise varied. There are days when we can see things clearly, days when we react more emotionally, days when we are more closely tied to logical processes in the mind. When performing the exercises, some people will intuitively choose the appropriate flower for the quality of a particular day. You should mentally devote the whole day to that flower. This doesn't mean that you should be actively doing exercises all day long, but rather allow the vibration of the flower principle to carry on "behind the scene" and be aware of how the concept is constantly manifested in and all around you.

There are days when you are very centred and days when you find it difficult to be in your centre. That, too, is normal; don't let yourself feel discouraged by this, but stick at the exercise to the best of your ability. You always have the option of working on the principle again and gaining new experience with it later, on a day with a different quality.

Do you have a lot of negative reactions?

If you notice a lot of negative feelings and associations in reaction to working on a particular flower, this generally indicates that you should be taking the flower concerned. In this case, take the flower by the glass-of-water method, and then later you should consider whether or not to incorporate it in the combination of flowers you are currently taking.

If you are concentrating on working through all 38 Bach flowers one after the other, you shouldn't take any personal combination at the same time.

The flower behind the flower

If you already know the Bach flowers well, you may become aware when doing an exercise that your negative experience with one particular flower is also tied in with other flower concepts: impressions of the flower you are working on at the time keep getting mixed up with images that fit in better with other flowers. For example, if you are working on *Vine*, *Pine* and *Larch* may also keep coming up.

Don't get irritated by this, just make a note of your associations and take the opportunity to track down your own personal pattern by making your next step to do some further work on these new flowers. If you work intensively on the flower concepts that come to the surface, step by step you can recognise and overcome the fundamental blockages in your development process.

Flower principles at different stages of problem solving

Each individual flower principle is linked with a different area of life or a different problem. When working on a particular problem you will encounter – from a psychological point of view – various completely different stages:

Initial awareness of a developing problem

The challenge posed by the problem

Resistance to the challenge

Solution of the problem

Solutions worked out for the problem are tested again by setbacks.

You will experience the flower principles with differing degrees of intensity depending on which stage you are currently at. If you carry on working continuously with the flower principles, new aspects of the basic problem will keep presenting themselves, since these developments are fluid.

7
THE 38 BACH FLOWER PRINCIPLES AND THE EXPERIENTIAL PROGRAMME

1. AGRIMONY
THE HONESTY FLOWER

1. How can I tell when I am in the negative *Agrimony* state?

By thoughts like:
"Keep smiling."
"Nobody needs to know how I really feel."

By feelings like:
Agonies of inner restlessness.

By reactions like:
Bad news is immediately glossed over or suppressed.
Feeling compelled to take on the role of peacemaker in quarrels between two friends.

By energy qualities like:
Flat, sandwiched between pressure from inside and outside.

2. How does the disruption of communication with my inner guidance come about?

My **Feeling Self** has a strong desire for harmony and is overtaxed by experiencing a lot of painful emotions. Instead of processing these with the help of my **Thinking Self** and also turning to the Higher Self in the process, my **Feeling Self** retreats into an illusion of harmony.

It suppresses anything that could become painful and passes on to my **Thinking Self** only the images with pleasant colours.

The result of this is that my **Thinking Self** reinforces the false harmony.

3. Which mental truth does my Thinking Self either ignore or misunderstand?

Living in the world of polarity is at the same time both harmonious and disharmonious. Life energy is constantly flowing to and fro between these two poles.

We must take note of both poles and relate to them both. This is the only way we can really learn and develop further.

We experience true harmony and inner peace at moments when we have found our way to our Higher Self. We also need to direct our attention inwards instead of orienting ourselves to the outside world.

4. Which conscious decision or intuition will link me with my inner guidance again?

For example: I resolve to behave honestly towards myself and others and be trusting enough to develop a harmonious link with my Higher Self.

My inner guidance provides me with the strength to relate to the positive and negative events in life, to grow through them and to find inner peace.

5. Which qualities will help me here?

Trust, courage, sincerity.

6. How can I tell when my positive *Agrimony* potential is growing?

For example: *I am now more honest than before towards myself and others, and I have more strength to resolve conflicts.*

Ideal
Communication

1. Experience the negative *Agrimony* state as consciously as possible:

Mask on ... mask off ...

Look in a mirror and put on a happy expression. Feel the way your face muscles get more and more tense from this. Hold this tension for about two minutes whilst observing your feelings and thoughts.

Then allow the mask to drop and experience the way in which your facial expression changes. Where else in your body does tension subside? What feelings and thoughts do you have now?

In order to experience the difference between these two states even more intensively you can even repeat this exercise. Write your observations down in your Bach flowers journal.

Additional exercise before going to sleep

As you lie in bed, check your face for any elements of the mask still present and for any tensions left over from the day. Ask yourself: "Where did I tense up my face today? What tensions did I create on the inside and outside when I did this?" Then concentrate on one area of the face at a time and explore any tensions you may become aware of. Try to release these as consciously as possible as you breathe out.

2. Observe the *Agrimony* principle around you:

Go into a bar, to a circus or a musical. Pay a visit to an expensive perfume shop or a posh boutique. Allow yourself to soak up the atmosphere. Then inwardly take a step backwards and try to gain a sense of the people behind their masks. What fears or apprehensions might they even have in common with you?

Look at the mask of optimism donned by business people at the beginning of a meeting.

Maybe you can even think of people you know for whom everything is "no problem", who cover up their inner fears with misconceived positive thinking, maybe by listening to positive affirmation cassettes, instead of really exploring their feelings.

3. Discover and develop your positive *Agrimony* potential:

This exercise is about encouraging your **Feeling Self** to admit its feelings and fears to itself and to work on them with your **Thinking Self**.

Only then can the **Thinking Self** help you to see how you can deal more constructively with these feelings in the future.

The three-stage honesty plan

- First stage: After getting out of bed, stand on a chair or on the edge of the bed, set your timer to one minute and allow yourself to feel.

 Then say aloud how you are feeling at that moment, e.g.: *"I feel tense inside."*

 Or voice a fear about something in the day lying ahead of you, e.g.: *"I am scared about my discussion with Mrs N."* If you find you cannot sustain this exercise for a whole minute, try it again at another time.

- Second stage: Go into the bathroom now and express the same feelings in front of the mirror. Watch your face as you do this. How does it make you feel?

 Write these experiences down in your flowers journal and, if necessary, carry on working later with the *Mimulus* exercise (see page 159).

- Third stage: Talk honestly about your feelings or a deep fear with someone you trust. When you do this, don't let the other person distract or console you too soon, but try to work out a solution together if that is possible and worthwhile.

Additional recommendations

Now show your true face on the outside as well as inside. Forget your usual habits and try going shopping without any make-up or without combing your hair. Men could try turning up at an appointment unshaven or wearing extra-casual clothing.

Every day practise giving an honest answer to the question *"How are you?"* Instead of answering *"Fine, thanks"* as usual, try saying *"Not so good, actually."*

1   2   3   4   5   6   7   8   9   10   11   12

2. ASPEN
THE PSYCHIC FLOWER

1. How can I tell when I am in the negative *Aspen* state?

By thoughts like:
"I don't get it, it makes me scared."
"This atmosphere always makes me uncomfortable."
"I'm too sensitive."

By feelings like:
Uneasiness for no reason, an incomprehensible feeling of dread.
Sensing an imaginary danger.

By reactions like:
Not going into certain pubs because the atmosphere is too strange.
A child unable to get to sleep and insisting on keeping the light on because it is afraid of nightmares.
Fear of going into the cellar alone.

By energy qualities like:
Too open.
Slight excited tension from behind.
The inner antennae sense an unfamiliar darkness.

2. How does the disruption of communication with my inner guidance come about?

My **Feeling Self** is hypnotised by negative internal images and unconscious fear associations. It is unable to deal with these and remains awkwardly where it is because it doesn't summon either my Higher Self or my **Thinking**

Self to help.

Because of this, my **Thinking Self** remains helpless and inactive. Perceptions cannot be checked for their reality content and classified. Everything hangs in the balance and no learning process takes place.

3. Which mental truth does my Thinking Self either ignore or misunderstand?

The Higher Self confronts us on our path through life with various consciousness experiences according to the needs of our individual growth process.

We have to consciously train and develop our instruments for perception so that we can distinguish impressions from the outside world from inner, imaginary fear impulses.

If we accept this challenge we will be able to incorporate more and more "inner shadows", and through this process we will gain in strength.

4. Which conscious decision or intention will link me with my inner guidance again?

For example: I resolve to turn my ear inwards in indeterminable situations, to move forwards, to turn on my objective, rational side, and to ask my Higher Self for protection.

5. Which qualities will help me here?

Courage, decisiveness and the ability to differentiate.

6. How can I tell when my positive *Aspen* potential is growing?

For example: *I can distinguish more easily between different levels of consciousness. I can recognise more and more positively whether a feeling comes from within myself or whether I am picking it up from outside.*

Ideal
Communication

1. Experience the negative *Aspen* state as consciously as possible:

The scary place

Go somewhere that you find unpleasant or frightening like a dark cellar, a warehouse, a cemetery, a lonely piece of woodland or similar, and analyse your impressions.

Stage 1: Make your first visit in daylight or electric light in order to familiarise yourself a bit with the surroundings you plan to visit later in the dark. If you have decided on a place that is not in your house, take an escort along with you, who should keep at a safe distance behind you.

Stage 2: Now visit your scary place in the dark. For example, go down into the cellar with a torch and imagine yourself as a child again. Allow the objects on the walls to assume an independent life in the light from the torch, turning into threatening beings or even ghosts. Pay attention to sounds: crackling, dripping, rustling. Can you smell how musty it is? What feelings or fantasies of fear does this bring up in you? Note down your impressions and suppositions. Example: *"I see a large, dark box. It creaks and crackles. Maybe there's a person inside. I'm afraid he will do me harm. It smells fusty, like an old church"* etc.

Stage 3: Now switch the light on or revisit your place in daylight and note down in a sparse telegram style what you can now see, e.g.: *"Cellar, size approx. 13 sq. m, containing one wardrobe and several cases – stop – behind them a corner full of boxes, I can't remember what's in them – stop – must get them cleared out –*

stop – musty smell – caretaker must be informed."

Now carry on working with point 3.

2. Observe the *Aspen* principle around you:

Stand by the exit from a cinema where a horror film has just finished and watch the cinema-goers as they pour out. What do their eyes express?

Observe the behaviour of a group of tourists in a dungeon or burial chamber.

Take your children for a ride on a ghost train.

3. Discover and develop your positive *Aspen* potential:

Your **Feeling Self** must learn not to get stuck with the impressions provided by its feelings, but to enlist the help of the **Thinking Self** to interpret its sensitive perceptions correctly and to categorise them as "realistic" and "unrealistic." In this way you can gain more and more of a sense of security in your dealings with your own sensitivity, and in the long run build up a stable link with the Higher Self.

Admittedly, this process can take years, does require instruction and in some cases even therapeutic support.

Now continue with Exercise 1.

What is really going on?

Analyse your written notes from Exercise 1 and answer the following questions in sequence:

🔎 "What was I aware of?"
E.g.: "A crackling noise in the room."

🔎 "What feeling did this bring up in me and how did I react?"
"Fear, holding my breath, hairs standing up on the back of my neck."

🔎 "What was my first assumption?"
"There could be someone standing behind the cupboard."

🔎 "What was the reality when I went back and looked again in daylight?"
"The crackling noise came from the cupboard, I suppose because when I entered the cellar this affected the static charge of the cupboard."

🔎 "What will I do the next time I find myself in a similar situation?"
You should develop a personal decision based on point 4 (p. 85).

Additional recommendation

Whenever you have the feeling of wanting or having to protect yourself, you should always do one thing first: centre yourself. With your energy focused in your centre you can then surround yourself with protection based on your own imagination – e.g. in the form of a mantle of light.

1 2 3 4 5 6 7 8 9 10 11 12

3. BEECH
THE TOLERANCE FLOWER

**1. How can I tell when I am in the negative *Beech*
state?**

By thoughts like:
"I always find a hair in my soup."
"How on earth ..."

By feelings like:
Anxiety, feeling inwardly distant from others.

By reactions like:
Noticing straight away when anything is less than perfect.
Reacting critically or with false tolerance.
*Unexpected outbreaks of feeling in people I am talking to are
seen inwardly as an embarrassing faux pas.*

By energy qualities like:
"Touchy distancing", constriction.

**2. How does the disruption of
communication with my inner
guidance come about?**

My **Thinking Self** has repressed many
of my **Feeling Self**'s needs. If my **Thinking Self**
now tunes into these repressed needs as a result of
other people behaving in a corresponding way, it
tries to maintain the repression by criticising the
behaviour concerned in others.

In so doing, it doesn't orient itself by the
Higher Self but by theoretical
standards, which however do not ring
true with my **Feeling Self** and are often
hurtful to the feelings of other people.

3. **Which mental truth does my Thinking Self either ignore or misunderstand?**

Any devaluing criticism, whether spoken out loud or not, is an attack on another's personality, and at the same time causes a blockage in the higher cosmic energy field. It contradicts the Law of Unity.

Bach says: *"Every bad thing is a good thing at the wrong time and in the wrong place."*

4. **Which conscious decision or intention will link me with my inner guidance again?**

For example: *I resolve to observe situations with empathy before judging, and to pay attention to tuning into my own feelings in the process. At the same time I will try to gain a deeper understanding of the processes of growth on a higher level.*

5. **Which qualities will help me here?**

Openness, sympathy, capacity for empathy.

6. **How can I tell when my positive *Beech* potential is growing?**

For example: *I can observe situations without immediately judging them. I can look at them from several points of view and also recognise the positive in them.*

Ideal
Communication

1. Experience the negative *Beech* state as consciously as possible:

"Look for mistakes!"

In order to feel the *Beech* state, spend 45 minutes sitting on a crowded bus or metro train.

Put your clipboard on your lap and assess your fellow travellers by asking yourself: What's wrong here, what makes me feel uneasy? If I had to give marks out of 10, how many would I give this person?

Example: "*Young man in the corner, mid-twenties, unwashed hair, jacket too small, stubborn demeanour, overall mark satisfactory.*"

Or: "*Woman sitting next to me, about 35, wearing a somewhat careworn expression, smelling slightly of sweat (surely everyone can afford a deodorant nowadays!).*" And so on.

Be aware of how you feel when you adopt this negative point of view. Do you note any change in your body? Does your feeling about other people or about yourself change? How does your mood change?

In order to get yourself out of this destructive attitude you should now activate your powers of positive imagination. Imagine how these same people, whom you have just been tearing to pieces, might look and what effect they might have on you if they were in a very positive situation, e.g.: "*What impression would the unshaven man make later when he gets together with a new girlfriend he's just fallen in love with? What impression would the careworn woman make if I saw her on her holidays, sun-tanned and playing on the beach with her children?*"

Note how many negative points you found and how easy or difficult you found it to imagine the positive side.

2. Observe the *Beech* principle around you:

Study the opera reviews in a quality daily newspaper: "The coloraturas could have sparkled more." In a restaurant review we read: "Unfortunately, head chef X continues to celebrate a cuisine that lacks any kind of balance, subjecting diners to a gastronomic rollercoaster ride. Fried eel served with a thick rasher of streaky bacon is rather too profane for its price."

If we were called upon to criticise these critics, we may find something like the following on the tip of our tongues: "One might have wished their criticism to be a little more sensitive ..."

As to the question of who actually becomes a critic, the answer is quite simple: people with a yearning for beauty and perfection, yet without themselves possessing sufficient creativity to produce anything of much beauty.

Look around you and see whether anyone you know finds a hair in every bowl of soup, and if so, why.

3. Discover and develop your positive *Beech* potential:

My **Thinking Self** must be prepared to develop a link with my **Feeling Self**, get to know its own feelings and also be aware of the feelings of others.

Through my **Feeling Self** my **Thinking Self** can also gain a connection to my Higher Self and recognise that judgements are never absolute.

"Make your criticisms relative"

Think of a person or a situation you have been inwardly criticising for a long time.

For example: *"My colleague, X, is intrusive and not particularly intelligent."*

↝ How would you feel if something like that was said about you?
"I'd feel hurt."

↝ What is your criticism based on?
"When all the issues have actually been sorted out at a meeting, this colleague X keeps on asking questions, giving the impression that he hasn't grasped anything that was said before."

↝ Could there be any reason that you can't possibly be aware of or which you simply haven't thought of to explain this colleague's behaviour?
"X is responsible for the reports. Perhaps he often used to come in for criticism for leaving things out."

↝ What might be the positive aspect to the behaviour of the person you feel critical of?
"By asking all those questions, X forces everyone else to think certain problems through completely. Grey areas can still sometimes come to light through this process."

↝ Can you detect any similar traits in yourself which you have not yet done any conscious work on?
"Yes, until I have grasped something fully I tend to ask searching questions without thinking about the feelings of the person I am questioning."

Repeat this exercise every time you feel *Beech* feelings coming up.

1 2 3 4 5 6 7 8 9 10 11 12

4. CENTAURY
THE SERVICE FLOWER

1. How can I tell when I am in the negative *Centaury* state?

By thoughts like:
"One must fit in with others."
"What would you like me to do?"
"This is the way my Dad would like it."

By feelings like:
Inner weakness.
Inability to stand up to people more forceful than oneself.
Reactive rather than active.

By reactions like:
Saying yes even if we would really like to say no.
Friends always warning us: "You shouldn't let yourself be taken advantage of so much."

By energy qualities like:
Slack feeling inside, giving in to greater pressure.
Bones seemingly made of rubber.

2. How does the disruption of communication with my inner guidance come about?

My **Feeling Self** is looking for recognition by offering obedience and servitude.

    My **Thinking Self** misunderstands the principle of service. It confuses devotional service to the divine plan with responsible

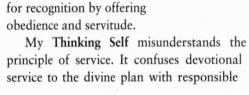

and conscious everyday service on the level of polar reality (see p. 29). It therefore does not dare to set limits for the excessive demands of other people through a clear decision of will.

Thus both **Feeling Self** and **Thinking Self** become less and less able to recognise and fulfil their own life plan.

(see p. 29)

3. Which mental truth does my Thinking Self either ignore or misunderstand?

We only serve the divine plan by fulfilling our own life plan.

4. Which conscious decision or intention will link me with my inner guidance again?

For example: *Before going along with what somebody else wants I will ask myself: "To what extent will this contribute to my own development and the other person's development, and to what extent will it benefit or harm the greater whole?" Only then will I make a decision and act upon it.*

5. Which qualities will help me here?

Independence, ability to differentiate, will-power.

6. How can I tell when my positive *Centaury* potential is growing?

For example: *I can recognise my own needs more readily, and more often do what I really want to.*

Ideal
Communication

1. Experience the negative *Centaury* state as consciously as possible:

"How am I too compliant"?

Try playing tug-of-war with a child or have a game with a young puppy with a stick in its mouth. Instead of trying to keep pulling for as long as possible, give in after a short while.

Take note of your feelings as you do this. Be aware that you are not actually playing the game properly at all, and check your opposite number's response to see whether or not it includes an element of disappointment.

Now set your timer for 15 minutes. Centre yourself, then write down in your flowers journal 3 to 5 situations in which you wanted to say no but, for one reason or another, were unable to.

You should record these situations in the following format:

Situation:

E.g. *"I couldn't say no when my mother asked me to plant out her balcony."*

↝ "Why didn't I say no?"
"Because I was afraid that she would reproach me."

↝ "What negative consequences resulted for me personally?"
"I didn't have time to prepare my lesson, and as a result the class was a shambles."

Now read through what you have written again and allow yourself to respond to the situations. How do you feel now? Note down your feelings in your flowers journal.

2. Observe the *Centaury* principle around you:

You may find that the following lament rings a bell:

"I've gone and let a door-to-door salesperson talk me into a magazine subscription even though we already get 3 other magazines delivered regularly!"

The following situation may also seem familiar: you find yourself at a dinner party and have already had plenty to eat when the host produces another delectable dessert and presses you politely to have some. Do you manage to decline?

Young girls from 5 to 7 are also often in a *Centaury* state. These are girls who are considered particularly well-behaved and who unconsciously want to ensure the goodwill of their teachers and relatives through obedience and gentleness.

3. Discover and develop your positive *Centaury* potential:

My **Feeling Self** needs to get back in touch with my Higher Self in order to centre itself and then get a feeling for whether other people's demands go against my own life plan.

My **Thinking Self** needs to develop and articulate its will, and above all learn to defend its own limits.

"Practise saying no"

Now continue with Exercise 1, choosing one of your examples. Prepare yourself for the next situation in which you can practise saying no.

"Stage 1: Write a dialogue. How could you answer the next time your mother asks you to do something that you can only manage by dropping something important to you?

Mother: *"If you don't want to plant out the balcony you might at least go and get me the plants from the garden centre."*

Daughter: *"No, I haven't even got time for that."*

Mother: *"Then at least tell me what I should plant."*

Daughter: *"Whose balcony is it, mine or yours? I'm going to stick with my no. I want to prepare my lesson, so you'll have to sort out your balcony yourself."*

Mother: *"Well, then I'll just have to ..."*

Finish each dialogue with your personal "I will –" statement:

"I, ... (your name), *will* ..." Thus, in our example:

"I, Jane Lewis, intend to prepare my lesson."

Stage 2: Stand in front of a mirror and read this dialogue out loud, observing any change in your facial expression and your entire posture. Note how more and more strength and conviction flow into your "Nos" until finally your whole personality is emanating this "No!"

Stage 3: Reward yourself for each "No." Set up a "will-box" for yourself and pay into it a small sum of money to put towards fulfilling a personal desire every time you achieve a "no-victory."

1   2   3   4   5   6   7   8   9   10   11   12

5. CERATO
THE INTUITION FLOWER

1. How can I tell when I am in the negative *Cerato* state?

By thoughts like:
"It can't be as simple as that."
"Is this the way to do it nowadays?"
"Other people know more about this than I do."

By feelings like:
Uncertainty, helplessness, doubt.

By reactions like:
After making a decision, seeking confirmation from other people that the decision is really the right one.
Pupils in a classroom work
"improving their work for the worse"
by introducing mistakes just before handing the work in.

By energy qualities like:
The energy runs off in various directions. The centre feels empty and irritated.

2. How does the disruption of communication with my inner guidance come about?

My **Feeling Self** is intimidated and irritated because my **Thinking Self** doubts the messages it sends and rejects them time after time.

My **Thinking Self** believes that it has to solve problems using reason alone. In so doing it dissipates its energy, because it always wants to find confirmation from the outside world in order not to have to bear the responsibility alone.

In this situation it becomes increasingly difficult for the Higher Self to make itself noticed.

3. **Which mental truth does my Thinking Self either ignore or misunderstand?**

The right answers for our own life plan are to be found not in the outside world but inside ourselves. The inner guidance expresses itself through the voice of intuition, in which feeling and reason work together.

4. **Which conscious decision or intention will link me with my inner guidance again?**

For example: If I am looking for a personal answer, I turn inwards and place my trust in the first message I receive, be it in the form of an image, idea, feeling or event.

5. **Which qualities will help me here?**

Courage, trust.

6. **How can I tell when my positive *Cerato* potential is growing?**

For example: *I can now form my own opinion more rapidly and stick to it.*

Ideal
Communication

1. Experience the negative *Cerato* state as consciously as possible:

"What would Aunt Anne say about this ..."

Think of a situation – not necessarily of any great importance – in which you will need to make a decision in the near future. Your bathroom fittings may, for example, be very old and may irritate you every time you look at them. You have to decide whether or not you want to invest a considerable amount of money to completely renovate and redecorate the bathroom.

Formulate the decision confronting you and write it down in the centre of a page in your flowers journal. Then, without pausing for thought, write the first answer that occurs to you spontaneously in small writing at the bottom of the page.

Now imagine if you were to consult six people from amongst your family and friends on your difficult decision, asking them to give you advice.

What answers do you think that you would receive? Write down the names of those offering advice along with their suggestions expressed as catchwords, writing them in a pattern of rays spreading out from your question, and as you do so, let these answers wash over you. How did this exercise make you feel? Do you feel enriched, nervous, divided, inwardly more and more confused? And are you now in a better position to make a decision?

Make a note of your impressions.

2. Observe the *Cerato* principle around you:

Some time try observing other people shopping, in an expensive boutique for example. When a customer has almost decided on a particular article of clothing, you will often see the sales assistant make them unsure again by bringing out clothes with a slightly different cut or even a completely different style.

There is almost certainly someone close to you who is always asking for help in making decisions: "Do you think it would be a good idea if I ...?"

3. Discover and develop your positive *Cerato* potential:

My **Thinking Self** needs to turn to my **Feeling Self** and gratefully acknowledge that if they work together well the right decisions can certainly be reached every time.

Now continue with Exercise 1.

My opinion ... my decision!

🔑 Stage 1: Now turn inwardly to your **Feeling Self**.

See what effects the advice of your six relatives and friends has on your **Feeling Self**, by allowing your feeling to concentrate in your solar plexus; in other words, be aware of your gut feeling.

List the various pieces of advice down the left-hand side of the page, and alongside each piece of advice put into words the feeling it produces in you.

Advice: *"Aunt Anne says I would be better advised to save the money"* – Feeling: "Feels unsatisfying."

"My sister recommends a cheap solution." – "Doesn't do anything for me."

"My husband wants to put things off, as always." – "This makes me feel angry."

"My friend Henry recommends that if you're going to start renovating, it's best to do the whole flat." – "This makes me feel weak at the knees."

"Elisabeth says I should negotiate with my landlord for him to reimburse me later, and then choose just what I like best." – "What a relief, that gives me a good feeling, OK!"

🔑 Stage 2: Now go on to analyse the different pieces of advice according to the following criteria:

"Which of these views did I actually already know in my subconscious?"

"Which suggestions actually solve not my problem but that of the person giving the advice?"

"Which pieces of advice would put me under pressure inwardly, giving me guilt feelings if I didn't follow them?" And so on.

🔑 Stage 3: Ask yourself: "How can I tell whether a decision is right for me or not?"

Perhaps by a particular bodily reaction – such as itching, or by a particular thought or inner feeling – such as joy or relief. Make a conscious connection between this awareness and a specific gesture such as pulling your left ear, thus creating your own personal ritual.

In future, use this feeling–movement combination as a criterion in making a decision.

1 2 3 4 5 6 7 8 9 10 11 12

6. CHERRY PLUM
THE OPENNESS FLOWER

1. How can I tell when I am in the negative *Cherry-Plum* state?

By thoughts like:
"It's enough to drive you mad."
"I feel as if I'm about to burst."

By feelings like:
Build-up of inner tension.
Fear of losing self-control.

By reactions like:
Desire to thump or kick someone along with the need to control those desires.

By energy qualities like:
Excessive, bottled-up pressure.

2. How does the disruption of communication with my inner guidance come about?

My **Thinking Self** organises an all-out defence to ward off the feeling impulses from my **Feeling Self** as it is afraid it won't be able to cope with the associated thoughts.

This blocks off my **Feeling Self**, which is then no longer able to receive any further impulses from the Higher Self. The learning process stagnates.

This avoidance strategy works until the inner tension becomes too strong and discharges at the wrong moment in time.

3. Which mental truth does my Thinking Self either ignore or misunderstand?

We are just a part of a larger whole, one small energy system in a greater energy system, a microcosm in the macrocosm.

Only if we keep the connection with the next system above us open by means of our inner guidance can we live and develop in harmony with it. Then we are secure and in the hands of God.

4. Which conscious decision or intention will link me with my inner guidance again?

For example: *The moment my mind loses its grip on a situation, I make a conscious decision to open myself to hear the advice from my Higher Self – and then act confidently in accordance with this inner guidance.*

5. Which qualities will help me here?

Willingness, trust, tolerance, patience.

6. How can I tell when my positive *Cherry-Plum* potential is growing?

For example: *I can recognise my own feeling impulses earlier, am better able to accept them and can express myself before too much tension has built up. Because of this, in many situations I react more calmly than before.*

Ideal
Communication

1. Experience the negative *Cherry-Plum* state as consciously as possible:

"Hoard up your feelings!"

Try stopping water flowing from a garden hose with your hand and see how long you can resist the pressure.

Or put yourself into the *Cherry-Plum* state with one of the following techniques: wear a blazer one size too small for a whole morning, or wear a pullover that is slightly too hot. Men could try doing up their belt two notches tighter than usual.

Note down in your flowers journal how things went for you in the course of the morning. What feelings and thoughts became blocked? Did you feel agitated? Did you even have to abandon the exercise?

2. Observe the *Cherry-Plum* principle around you:

It is fairly common to have been brought up not to display any intense feelings.

Many people find displays of intense emotion – such as can sometimes be seen between drivers in Italian city traffic – rather amusing. The *Cherry-Plum* state is particularly common when people are not allowed to show emotion because of their profession: for example amongst people working in a complaints department or amongst the police, who are provoked verbally or even physically. Even an outsider can see their forced pretence of calm and sense the rising temperature of their feelings inside.

3. Discover and develop your positive *Cherry-Plum* potential:

My **Feeling Self** must accept itself and give up feeling afraid of its own feelings and of the impulses of the Higher Self.

My **Thinking Self** must accept the existence of my **Feeling Self** and process its impulses willingly.

Both must feel confident that nothing can happen to harm us under the guidance of the Higher Self.

Learn to know and love your feelings

Practise getting involved with your feelings. Blocked feelings may become magnified in the following sequence: feeling of irritation – anger – rage – hate – destruction.

Such emotions are either channelled outwards or, worse still, inwards. The sooner we can recognise our feelings and bring them out, the less serious the backlog of feelings they will create in our internal system.

The following exercise is about getting to know your first feeling impulses. Find a small bell or similar object with which you can give signals quickly. Then pick up a magazine and browse through it, ringing the bell as soon as you become aware of any emotion.

- Allow yourself to become consciously aware of this feeling and accept it.
  E.g.: *"Aha, anxiety."*

- Say this feeling out loud.
  "I feel uneasy, anxious."

- Write the feeling down in your flowers journal.

- Act out the feeling by expressing it in several different ways, using different voices and volumes, perhaps even singing it with accompanying gestures.

- Analyse the feeling: how did the first associated impulse manifest itself, and through what kind of physical sensation?

  What was the headline or picture in the magazine that gave rise to this feeling?

  Trace the feeling still further back. When, and in what situation, have you experienced similar feelings before?

  What is this feeling trying to communicate to me, what impulse for a possible change does it want to give me?

  You should also carry out this exercise if strong feelings come up through other flower exercises.

Additional recommendations

Perform a shaking meditation, shaking out your feelings to dynamic music for 15 minutes. Chop some wood, work on a punch ball, play football or dance flamenco. Isometric exercises have also proved useful, where you increase the tension in specific groups of muscles before suddenly releasing it.

1   2   3   4   5   6   7   8   9   10   11   12

7. CHESTNUT BUD
THE LEARNING FLOWER

1. How can I tell when I am in the negative *Chestnut-Bud* state?

By thoughts like:
"It doesn't matter."
"After I've finished this I'll do x, then y, then z."

By feelings like:
Astonishment, inner drivenness, a feeling of being on an internal autopilot, indifference.

By reactions like:
Finding oneself time and time again in the same unsatisfactory situations without knowing how one got there.
Finding it hard to stay on the ball in conversations and unwittingly asking the same questions over and over again.

By energy qualities like:
The energy is pushing forwards from the back of the neck.
Energy "blackouts."

2. How does the disruption of communication with my inner guidance come about?

My **Feeling Self** no longer wants to be reminded of negative experiences and tries to block them out.

My **Thinking Self** does not take the trouble to find out the reasons behind this, preferring instead to put up with the fact that the same thing happens again the next time a similar situation arises. This leads to a never-ending *"stop-start effect"* in the learning process. Subconsciously the same automatic patterns result time and time again. Any new impulses from your Higher Self cannot be taken on board.

3. **Which mental truth does my Thinking Self either ignore or misunderstand?**

Everything that happens has a different significance and conceals an opportunity for development.

But we must complete our sequences of action, conclude our learning processes and draw every possible mental lesson from each experience in order to make the most of it in our development.

Allowing ourselves to make the same mistakes over and over again amounts to a "waste of cosmic energy", as the "economic principle" is equally valid on a universal level.

4. **Which conscious decision or intention will link me with my inner guidance again?**

For example: *Under the guidance of my Higher Self I decide to behave more co-operatively from now on in the school of life, to pay closer attention and to consider the possible consequences before acting.*

5. **Which qualities will help me here?**

Willingness to engage in mental struggle, will to learn, inner consistency.

6. **How can I tell when my positive *Chestnut-Bud* potential is growing?**

For example: *I recognise my own automatic reaction patterns. I have a better understanding of why I do what I do, and I am improving that understanding day by day.*

Ideal
Communication

1. Experience the negative *Chestnut-Bud* state as consciously as possible:

"Wash your hands by the clock"

In the *Chestnut-Bud* state one is governed by an internal autopilot. Get yourself into that state as follows:

Set your timer for 15 minutes. Go to the bathroom and wash your hands in the usual manner. Quite automatically wet them, lather, rinse, dry and moisturise them. Carry out this sequence of actions at a brisk pace, then carry on repeating the whole sequence until the 15 minutes are up.

As you do this, take note of anything at all you are still aware of. Are you aware of the way your thoughts begin increasingly to wander and how you are performing more and more automatically? Write down a few notes about the exercise in your flowers journal.

2. Observe the *Chestnut-Bud* principle around you:

Nearly everyone moans about habits they would like to break – from habitual throat clearing to nail biting and the like. In order to observe the *Chestnut-Bud* state it is important to recognise the small yet decisive moment in which a person slips back into his or her automatic behaviour again. It is, of course, easier to recognise this moment in others than in yourself.

If you work for the same company for a long time, you soon find out the situations in which your workmates slip into unconscious behaviour patterns. One may always react too quickly while another will react too slowly. One will begin to stammer while another will need to become aggressive before being able to accept instructions.

Do you know the television sketch *"Dinner for One?" Year in, year out, on New Year's Eve millions of watchers wait with bated breath for the butler to keep tripping up over the tiger's head.*

3. Discover and develop your positive *Chestnut-Bud* potential:

My **Thinking Self** must move towards my **Feeling Self** and encourage it to turn to the Higher Self again, secure in the knowledge that it will always receive constructive learning impulses from this part.

My **Thinking Self** must also be prepared to process these impulses in order for learning processes to take place.

Now continue with Exercise 1.

"Break down an automatic action: The Tao of washing hands"

Now wash your hands one more time, but this time in slow motion. Observe the process meticulously and describe the individual phases of the washing process in your flowers journal in the way that a scriptwriter would describe them.

Thus, for example: *"I turn on the tap with my right hand and wet my hands. Then, also with my right hand, I pick up the soap, lather my hands, then thoroughly rinse the soap off again. I then take the towel in my left hand and use it to dry my hands ..."*

Can you now see that when you consciously watch every detail of an action, you have the opportunity to alter the process at any time?

Start to discover recurring mistakes or tiresome habits and then to change them by answering the following questions:

- "Which tiresome habit or which mistake would I like to free myself of?"
  "Failing to turn off the bath tap fully."

- "Under what circumstances does this tendency become more pronounced or frequent?"
  "When I'm in a hurry, and my mind has already moved on to the next task."
  The next time you make this mistake, have a look to see what's going on in your mind.

- "How exactly does it come about when I do that?"
  "I'm already reaching for the towel with my left hand, and I start drying myself at the same time as giving the tap a cursory turn with my right hand."

- "What could I change in order to put an end to this automatic behaviour?"
  "I could hang the towel far enough away to make myself move away from the washbasin before drying my hands."

- "When shall I start this new routine?"
  "The next time I wash my hands!"
  Do some work on any other bad habits you may have such as habitual lateness, interrupting other people when they're speaking, noisy eating ... and outwit yourself by devising some tricks to help correct these habits.

1   2   3   4   5   6   7   8   9   10   11   12

8. CHICORY
THE MOTHERLINESS FLOWER

1. How can I tell when I am in the negative *Chicory* state?

By thoughts like:
"This is my due."
"I'm owed for that."

By feelings like:
Hunger for appreciation. Feeling neglected, unloved.
Feeling obligated. Fear that relationships may change.

By reactions like:
Giving something in order to receive something else in return, e.g.
calling round on your neighbour with a bottle of wine in order to
entice him to repair the faulty bell system without any objection.
"Helper syndrome."

By energy qualities like:
Emptiness in the centre.
Energy seemingly locked in different
directions.

2. How does the disruption of communication with my inner guidance come about?

My **Feeling Self** is spiritually
undernourished and is hungry for attention. To make up the deficit, however,
it turns not to my Higher Self but to my
Thinking Self.

My **Thinking Self** turns itself into a tool of the **Feeling Self**. It uses all the capabilities at its disposal to satisfy the never-ending emotional needs of the **Feeling Self** – and, if need be, by force.

3. **Which mental truth does my Thinking Self either ignore or misunderstand?**

Love is available all around, and the supply of love is inexhaustible if we can discover the link with the divine source of love inside ourselves with the help of the Higher Self. Because of the fact that, according to the law of resonance, we attract the same as we give out, we will then also find love in return in the outside world.

Manipulation of other people's feelings contravenes the Law of Unity as it interferes with the life plans of others. Anything we produce by force in this way will sooner or later be taken away from us again.

4. **Which conscious decision or intention will link me with my inner guidance again?**

For example: *I'd decide to accept that I can neither control nor hold onto other people's feelings. I recognise that I cannot find what I am looking for and also deserve in another person, but that I can get in direct touch through my inner guidance with the inexhaustible source of love.*

I respect every person's need to fulfil his or her own life plan.

5. **Which qualities will help me here?**

Respect, wisdom.

6. **How can I tell when my positive *Chicory* potential is growing?**

For example: *I follow my own personal needs, have become inwardly richer and less dependent on having the feelings of others directed at me.*

Ideal
Communication

1. Experience the negative *Chicory* state as consciously as possible:

"How can I get someone to ..."

It is hardly necessary in fact to practise this state because nearly everyone experiences or suffers it on a daily basis, sometimes in their private lives and certainly at work.

Create a short dialogue consisting of about 6 sentences as follows: You would like to achieve a specific objective but want to avoid expressing your wish directly, preferring instead to use roundabout means to get another person to fulfil this wish for you.

For example: After a busy day at the office you feel too tired to cook and would like to get your partner to come out for a meal with you.

You: *"Have you seen the beautiful awning at that Italian restaurant on the corner?"*

Partner: *"What awning, which corner?"*

You: *"A new Italian restaurant has opened up on the corner and Nina told me she had a very enjoyable evening there and that their tiramisu is out of this world."*

Partner *(who loves tiramisu, and now therefore paying rather more attention):* *"Tiramisu?"*

You: *"They also have some quite cheap set meals, but they are bound to be fully booked tonight. They're queuing up to get a table down there ..."*

Partner *(fired up by the apparent resistance):* *"What do you mean, fully booked? Let's just go over there and see ..."*

2. Observe the *Chicory* principle around you:

The positive *Chicory* potential is a manifestation of the female creative energy that has to a large extent been systematically repressed over the past several thousand years. This is why the negative *Chicory* state as a distorted form of creative self-expression is so widespread.

Look at the way in which adults often pick up a little child and "give it a cuddle" without asking. How do you suppose the child feels about this, and what is the adult looking to get from his or her action?

Now look at what parents promise their children in order to be left in peace and enjoy an undisturbed evening or take note of what people use to threaten others with, or what some people will do when they want something in particular: *"If I buy her that expensive belt, maybe she'll be particularly nice to me."* Or: *"If I get close to his best friend and if he starts fancying me, perhaps then at last he'll get round to proposing to me."*

3. Discover and develop your positive *Chicory* potential:

My **Feeling Self** must acknowledge the existence of my Higher Self and have faith in its guidance. My **Thinking Self** must encourage and support my **Feeling Self** on this path.

The following exercise is intended to help you to recognise your own needs better and to encourage you to satisfy your own wishes yourself by direct means.

"What do I really want?"

Write down the answers to the following questions for yourself in your flowers journal:

- "What situations do I interfere in?"
  E.g.: *"When my children are planning their holidays. I try to make them enthusiastic to travel to Egypt."*

- "What positive things do I want others to get from this?"
  "I want to organise for them unforgettable impressions and wonderful stimulation."
  "Can they develop satisfactorily without me being involved in this way?"
  "Yes."

- "What positive things do I want to get from this?"
  "I would like to be involved in planning the holiday and maybe even to travel with them."

- "Is there another way in which I could satisfy this need more directly?"
  "I could join a group that has an interest in Egypt and organises study trips there. If I did this, I would get to know some other people who share my interests."

Try to identify 10 personal needs in this way over the course of a month. Work out a plan for systematically satisfying these desires – without roundabout means involving others – one after the other.

1   2   3   4   5   6   7   8   9   10   11   12

9. CLEMATIS
THE REALITY FLOWER

1. How can I tell when I am in the negative *Clematis* state?

By thoughts like:
"Where exactly am I?"
"It would be nice if ..."
"It would be good to ..."

By feelings like:
Not being fully in the here and now.
Spiritually absorbed, swaying as if up in the clouds.
Absent-mindedness.

By reactions like:
Not knowing what the person you're talking to has just said.
Not having full possession of one's physical intuition, e.g. knocking against the edge of tables.
Going off on an inner fantasy at every opportunity.
Not being greatly affected by news,
regardless of whether it is good or bad.

By energy qualities like:
Invisible semicircular band stretching
from ear to ear around the back
of the head.
Bioenergetic field partially
dislocated from the
physical body.
Hands and feet lacking
in energy.

2. How does the disruption of communication with my inner guidance come about?

My **Feeling Self** flees from experiences that may be hurtful into more pleasant illusions.

My **Thinking Self** reacts to these pictures as if in a trance and has suspended activity. Thus my Higher Self is unable to make its presence felt.

3. Which mental truth does my Thinking Self either ignore or misunderstand?

The aim of our physical existence is to receive, understand and implement the Higher Self's ideas and plans. Any other use of cosmic energy is of no benefit either to our own development or to the greater whole.

4. Which conscious decision or intention will link me with my inner guidance again?

For example: *I decide to wake up from my dreams and take an active step into real life. I will test my inner pictures in reality and make what is sensible come true.*
I will draw the necessary strength for this task from my Higher Self.

5. Which qualities will help me here?

Presence, decisiveness, stamina.

6. How can I tell when my positive *Clematis* potential is growing?

For example: *Since I have started spending more time consciously engaged with reality, my life has become richer, more powerful and more satisfying.*

Ideal
Communication

1. Experience the negative *Clematis* state as consciously as possible:

"Retreat into a dream world!"

Buy yourself a trashy pulp-fiction novel on a subject which holds a moderate level of interest for you – e.g. medical, crime, romance – or a novel set where you were brought up. Read the first 15 pages, entering as consciously as possible into this world. Feel the way in which you increasingly lose your grip on the here and now ...

Then stop and read the same 15 pages again, this time using a highlighter pen to mark all the places of seductive clichés which contradict reality.

Now make a note in your flowers journal of how long this exercise took you and which of the day's real tasks you could have seen to in the course of this time.

2. Observe the *Clematis* principle around you:

We encounter the *Clematis* principle wherever we go. You need only observe the faces of people having to stand quietly in a queue. Can you recall waking someone from a deep sleep, when their reaction is delayed and a large part of their consciousness is still somewhere outside their physical body? Watch a group of children who are engrossed in the game they are playing and are living fully in the world of their dolls and characters. When they have to break off the game they often need several minutes to find their way back to reality again.

People who are entangled in a lie do not meet the eyes of the person they are talking to, or their look is veiled. They are looking inwards at the illusory world they spend their time in.

3. Discover and develop your positive *Clematis* potential:

With the assistance of my **Thinking Self**, my **Feeling Self** must recognise the fact that it cannot dream up the ideal world it is seeking, but that it can only experience such a world by turning to the Higher Self.

My **Thinking Self** must make the decision to actively support my **Feeling Self** in processing events from the real world, and then it must act on this decision. To do this it must develop its will.

"Make a daydream come true"

Write down 3 to 5 of your typical daydreams or pipe dreams in your flowers journal, then select one of them to work on.

Example:

"Buying a house in Provence and creating a lavender garden there."

Next, try to answer the following questions:

- "What is the real need behind my dream?"

  "To live out the creative side of my personality."

- "What is the likelihood, expressed as a percentage, that I will be able to fulfil this dream?"

  "5%."

- "What factors weigh in against the fulfilment of this dream?"

  "Not having enough money."

- "How would I have to modify the dream to enable it to be fulfilled?"

  "Instead of buying, I could rent such a house for 2 years."

- "How would I feel after realising this dream?"

  "Very content, full of joie de vivre."

- "What are the first steps I would need to take in order to make the dream come true?"

  "Look at any suitable properties advertised by local estate agents."

- "How would I feel while I am doing this?"

  "Excited, charged up with energy."

Supplementary recommendations

People who have a tendency towards *Clematis* states should consider the following fundamental questions:

- "When do I have a higher level of energy and personal strength at my command? …"

  "… when I am just imagining something?"

  "… or when I am actually realising an idea in practical terms?"

- "When is my physical constitution more robust? …"

  "… when I am just imagining something?"

  "… or when I am actually realising an idea in practical terms?"

- "When am I more helpful towards my fellow human beings? …"

  "… when I am just imagining something?"

  "… or when I am actually realising an idea in practical terms?"

  See if you can find even more reasons why it is more rewarding to live in the real world.

1   2   3   4   5   6   7   8   9   10   11   12

10. CRAB APPLE
THE CLEANSING FLOWER

1. How can I tell when I am in the negative *Crab-Apple* state?

By thoughts like:
"This mess makes me feel anxious."
"The smallest details must be right too."
"I feel disgusted by ..."

By feelings like:
Despondency, irritation.
Feeling clogged up, unclean, sticky.

By reactions like:
Feeling the need to take a shower to "feel yourself" again after a meeting in which one felt uncomfortable with the other people. The doorbell is ringing insistently. On the way to the door one notices some scraps of paper lying on the floor and feels unable to open the door before picking them up and putting them in the wastepaper basket.

By energy qualities like:
A slight feeling of stagnation and irritation throughout the body.

2. How does the disruption of communication with my inner guidance come about?

My **Feeling Self** has lost its link with the Higher Self and is suffering from feelings of disorder, repugnance and nausea.

My **Thinking Self** wants to help but tries to satisfy these demands for order and purity primarily on the level of polarity. Thus it imposes order according to limited standards and becomes over-fixated on unimportant details.

3. Which mental truth does my Thinking Self either ignore or misunderstand?

Divine order and perfection is not a static thing but a harmonious and ever-moving process in which every tiny detail is involved in a process of constant change.

What appears perfect today (e.g. a newly-completed house) was recently still an imperfect thing (building site), and will soon no longer be perfect (manifestations of wear and tear).

The more we can free ourselves from becoming fixated on outward details and can focus on the higher-level rhythms and patterns of order, the more these patterns can become established within ourselves as well as manifesting themselves on the outside.

4. Which conscious decision or intention will link me with my inner guidance again?

For example: *I decide to let go of my narrow ideas about order and cleanliness, to recognise instead the higher-level cosmic principles of order more and more, and to get in tune with them.*

5. Which qualities will help me here?

Generosity, charity and trust.

6. How can I tell when my positive *Crab-Apple* potential is growing?

For example: *I don't feel so wound up by apparent imperfections in the everyday world and in my body. I am coming to recognise more and more higher-level principles of order, and I take pleasure in them.*

Ideal
Communication

1. **Experience the negative *Crab-Apple* state as consciously as possible:**

"Long live chaos!"

Go out of your way to spend a weekend – or longer, if you can stand it – in chaos: forget about bodily hygiene, leave the tidying up, don't take the rubbish out. Don't bother to air your flat. Now find a magnifying glass, find a spot on your own skin and examine it adoringly with the glass.

You will soon sense how this chaos and uncleanliness begin to disturb you to the extent that you are no longer able to think about anything else, and you are left with only one fervent desire: to restore the order you are accustomed to.

How long did it take you to reach this point?

First allow yourself to take a hot shower, clear up, and when you are feeling better, record your experience in your flowers journal.

2. **Observe the *Crab-Apple* principle around you:**

In the *Crab-Apple* state the **Feeling Self** has lost its relationship with its own nature. This can be seen particularly in the western industrial nations and in Japan, where the trend for hygiene takes on increasingly extreme forms.

Note any examples of the *Crab-Apple* state in your own circle of friends and acquaintances. It can be seen in action in the people who simply can't stop cleaning their house, and in the office worker whose desk is as painfully clean as an operating table. *Crab-Apple* tendencies can also be seen in a business meeting when the agenda has to be followed to the letter even though some of the points have been covered in the meantime.

People who cannot touch door handles unless they are wearing gloves, or who feel unable to use a toilet other than in their own home, are distorting the *Crab-Apple* principle to an extreme degree.

Now look at *Crab-Apple* states in the world of nature. For example, you will notice that in your body everything is going on all at the same time: digestion, assimilation and elimination.

Roses thrive especially well and present us with sweet-smelling blooms when they are fed with rotted dung! Events in the natural world take place cyclically – and so, too, does human life: the newborn baby starts life soiling its nappies, and the old man often ends up back in the same situation again.

3. **Discover and develop your positive *Crab-Apple* potential:**

By turning to the Higher Self my **Feeling Self** must regain the connection with its own nature and through this lose its feelings of disgust.

My **Thinking Self** must support my **Feeling Self** in this process by recognising the higher-level principles of order.

My **Thinking Self** and **Feeling Self** have to accept that ideal order and perfection exist only on the level of the Higher Self.

"Which detail disturbs me?"

Answer the following questions in your flowers journal:

- "Which detail disturbs me?"
    "The dandruff on the shoulders of my colleague's jacket."

- "Does this detail have a positive side, and what process does this detail form a part of?"
    "Firstly, dandruff prevents hair loss, as shedding flakes of old skin from the head enables the scalp to breathe again. It serves a useful purpose in the metabolism of the skin."

- "Which higher-level pattern emerges from behind this process?"
    "The constant renewal of the human body."

- "What would you have done previously if this detail had irritated you?"
    "I would have turned my back in disgust or pointedly drawn my colleague's attention to the dandruff."

- "Do you see this detail now from a different point of view?"
    "Yes, because dandruff is in reality a quite natural thing."

- "How are you now able to behave in respect of this detail?"
    "I could perhaps recommend a natural-health remedy to my colleague which would correct the metabolic problem, and I could give him or her the address of a specialist."

1   2   3   4   5   6   7   8   9   10   11   12

11. ELM
THE RESPONSIBILITY FLOWER

1. How can I tell when I am in the negative *Elm* state?

By thoughts like:
"I'm not up to this job."
"I'm out of my depth here."
"I just don't know any more where to begin."

By feelings like:
Inadequacy, dejection, despondency, defensiveness.

By reactions like:
Feeling that one has chosen the wrong career when becoming overburdened at work.

By energy qualities like:
Empty feeling in the chest.
Energy largely divorced from the body as if it has flowed to another level.

2. How does the disruption of communication with my inner guidance come about?

My **Thinking Self** has overidentified itself with a particular task and has neglected the link with my **Feeling Self**. As a result, the moderating and intuitive impulses from my Higher Self can no longer reach my **Thinking Self** via my **Feeling Self**.

My **Thinking Self** now gets temporarily to an impasse in terms of strength in which it does not believe itself to be up to the task. The process of development is put on hold.

3. Which mental truth does my Thinking Self either ignore or misunderstand?

It is enough if we can fulfil our life task in a "humanly reasonable" framework in which all the different parts of the personality come into their own and are able to grow.

As human beings we cannot take on responsibility for the "greater whole" but only for our own life plan.

If we work in co-operation with our inner guidance we will notice when we have overstepped the mark with our ideas.

If we ask for help, it will come of its own accord because our life plan does not demand that we make any superhuman sacrifices.

4. Which conscious decision or intention will link me with my inner guidance again?

For example: *I decide to take my Feeling Self's needs far more seriously from now on, and to apply human rather than superhuman standards to the fulfilment of my tasks.*

If I have done my best I can be confident that things will turn out all right.

5. Which qualities will help me here?

Confidence, self-respect, creativity, composure.

6. How can I tell when my positive *Elm* potential is growing?

For example: *I take more notice of my personal needs than before and have more strength to carry out my tasks in life.*

Ideal
Communication

1. Experience the negative *Elm* state as consciously as possible:

"Do I have a task ... or am I my task?"

Think back to a situation in which you had taken on an unfamiliar task whose outcome was important not only to you personally but to other people too.

Example: You have said that you are willing to **single-handedly** organise a picnic for your son's classmates' teachers and parents in order to carry out an informal exchange of experience.

What are all the things that need to be done in order to carry out this task properly?

Set your timer for 10 minutes and compile a list of key points.

How do you feel as you write this list?

At the last moment you learn that the task has assumed even greater importance because the school's head teacher has decided to take part in this event.

How do you feel now? Does the task become larger in psychological terms as a result of this? Do you start feeling discouraged or even asking yourself whether you are up to the task at all?

Make a note of how you feel in your flowers journal.

2. Observe the *Elm* principle around you:

The *Elm* state is often experienced by people who have taken on a lot of, or too much, responsibility for a task. This state is not always easy to recognise from the outside.

Experience has shown people in the following positions to be particularly prone to the *Elm* state: single parents; mothers who are at the same time career women; people holding responsible positions in public life; schoolchildren who are supposed to do a lot of difficult homework after a long day at school; people who help others at times of emergency.

3. Discover and develop your positive *Elm* potential:

My **Thinking Self** must turn to my **Feeling Self** – liberate itself from exaggerated perceptions of its role, thus setting up a link with my Higher Self in order to become aware of its directing impulses again.

"Stay human ..."

Now carry on working on Exercise 1. Clarify in your own mind that the *Elm* state has come about as a result of the starting situation changing.

Tasks start to feel "more important" as soon as you yourself or others treat them as such. In such situations we often tend to imagine the task to be more difficult to fulfil than it really is.

Now carry on working on this issue, using a real task that you have in your life at present. See if you can answer the following questions:

- "What level of importance do I attach to this task? What level of importance does it have for other people in my circle of friends?"

- "How important is this task when viewed from a higher level?"

- "What impulses from my inner guidance are making their presence felt: what would I like to do – and what am I really capable of doing?"

- "What kind of help could I mobilise for carrying out this task?"

- "What would happen if I didn't take on this task at all?"

Again, write a list of keywords in answer to the questions above.

Supplementary recommendation for Elm candidates: delegate responsibility!

Within your family or circle of colleagues, practice delegating certain smallish tasks that you have always taken on by yourself in the past: get your partner to do the washing once in a while, or get your children to feed and walk the dog.

Use the time you gain in this way as consciously as possible to satisfy some of your personal needs.

On no account, however, should you worry yourself about how the others will perform the task you have delegated. Have confidence that everything will turn out all right even if perhaps differently from when you have done it until now.

Starting today, practise fulfilling your tasks in such a way that there is also enough space for more personal activities.

You should also recognise that the people around you will have more opportunity to learn if you pass on parts of jobs to them.

1 2 3 4 5 6 7 8 9 10 11 12

12. GENTIAN
THE BELIEF FLOWER

1. **How can I tell when I am in the negative *Gentian* state?**

By thoughts like:
"Of course it was bound to go wrong!"
"I can't believe it!"
"I said all along that this would happen!"
"I must say I'm sceptical about that."

By feelings like:
Uncertainty, disappointment, feeling depressed, inwardly careworn.

By reactions like:
Feeling vindicated, almost relieved even, when your doubts are confirmed and things go wrong.
When the first setbacks present themselves in a project, taking this as an indication that you should drop the entire project.

By energy qualities like:
Tension at the back of the head.
Energy level sinking below the heart.

2. **How does the disruption of communication with my inner guidance come about?**

My **Feeling Self** has had many disappointing experiences and fends off further experiences to avoid being disappointed again.

Instead of using its powers of reason to see these experiences in perspective, my **Thinking Self** identifies with and generalises them.

This gives rise to a lasting mistrust that is even applied to all the positive impulses from my Higher Self.

3. Which mental truth does my Thinking Self either ignore or misunderstand?

The path through life unfolds as a wave, leading through peaks and troughs.

There are bound to be setbacks in any process of development, their role being to help us to set our sights more accurately on the next step.

If we allow ourselves to be guided by the Higher Self and are prepared to keep going, we will master whatever difficulties may arise and emerge from them strengthened and enriched.

4. Which conscious decision or intention will link me with my inner guidance again?

For example: *I decide to view life from a broad and positive perspective, to fundamentally accept the sense of the development process, to accept the rough with the smooth and to ask for and allow help from my Higher Self.*

5. Which qualities will help me here?

Trust, faith, humility, endurance.

6. How can I tell when my positive *Gentian* potential is growing?

For example: *I am more optimistic than before and approach life with greater confidence.*

Ideal
Communication

1. Experience the negative *Gentian* state as consciously as possible:

"Sceptical attitude"

We have all at some time or other in our lives had disappointing experiences that have caused us either to think or to say aloud: *"I find it hard to hang on to my belief that human beings are good."*

Write down 5 such situations, select one of them for this exercise, and then answer the following questions:

Example:

"I am sceptical about our chance of finding a new flat that matches what we want."

🔑 "Which objective facts cause me to be sceptical?"

"There are hardly any nice flats available, and the prices are too high."

🔑 "What personal experience lies behind this attitude?"

"It took us two years of flat-hunting before we found our current flat, we experienced the many disappointments felt by most people engaged in this task, yet still we managed to choose the wrong flat!"

🔑 "What general conclusion did I draw from this?"

"Finding a suitable flat is an enormous problem. It simply never works out right."

🔑 "What is my present attitude to this situation as a result?"

"We simply stay on in our unsatisfactory living conditions."

How do you feel when you read through that last statement? Do you notice the mental and emotional constriction? Note down your feelings in your flowers journal.

2. Observe the *Gentian* principle around you:

Every group has its own "doubting Thomas" or sceptic who – whatever the suggestion – immediately spells out all the negative aspects of the matter and advises strongly against it. *"Yes, but I have had bad experience with that kind of thing"* their negative plea often begins. Surely he or she must have heard of the phenomenon of self-fulfilling prophecy?

In the *Gentian* state, one-off setbacks and small failures are generalised, and this can lead to chronic discouragement. Some people are more prone than others to this tendency. It can be seen at an early stage, in the classroom: some children simply start from the beginning again if they make a mistake doing their sums, while for others it is the end of the world each time. At such moments the latter children despair of ever being able to manage arithmetic. Even the suggestion that everyone learns it sooner or later is unable to provide any consolation at these moments.

3. Discover and develop your positive *Gentian* potential:

Rather than reacting straight away with a loss of heart, my **Feeling Self** must turn to my Higher Self and place trust in it. My **Thinking Self** must understand that learning processes take place in cycles and waves and that individual steps should not be generalised.

Free yourself from your sceptical attitude: continue from Exercise 1.

Has there ever been a situation which turned out well despite my scepticism?

Can you think of a situation in which the outcome was successful even though you secretly had doubts about it beforehand? If so, replay that situation now in order to draw a lesson from it to apply in the future and ask yourself the following questions:
Example:
"I surprised myself by finding a holiday flat in a short space of time."

↝ "Why was I sceptical?"
"I was worried that it would be a repeat of the experience I had searching for a flat in the city."

↝ "What happened differently from what you were expecting?"
"On my very second day of flat-hunting I met a woman by chance who, to my surprise, was looking for someone to let her holiday flat to."

↝ "What positive element did I personally contribute to this outcome?"
"I adjusted to the new situation straight away, pushed all my previous negative experiences to one side, and signed the contract."

↝ "What lesson can I draw from this?"
"Every situation is different, and Robert Burns was quite right when he observed: 'The best laid schemes o' mice an' men gang aft a-gley'."

Supplementary recommendation

Ponder on the words of Theodor Fontane:
"You should hear the music of life, most people hear only the dissonance."

1 2 3 4 5 6 7 8 9 10 11 12

13. GORSE
THE HOPE FLOWER

1. How can I tell when I am in the negative *Gorse* state?

By thoughts like:
"There's just no point in this any more."
"What good can come of it?"
"I've missed the boat."

By feelings like:
Resignation.
Feeling of inner tiredness, depression.

By reactions like:
*Inability in difficult situations to conceive that matters could take
a turn for the better again.*
*An example is a person who has got used to suffering from a
chronic illness and is living with it, but without accepting it.*

By energy qualities like:
Lack of energy, inner immobility.
Heaviness pulling downwards.

2. How does the disruption of communication with my inner guidance come about?

Negative circumstances in life are perceived by my
Thinking Self as so bad that it has decided to give
up trying. It is stuck firmly on the negative side
of reality and counters the impulses
from my **Feeling Self** and my inner
guidance with passive resistance.

The result of this is that even those positive opportunities for development which are still available are no longer perceived, and opportunities for change no longer seen.

The energy flow gradually comes to a stop.

3. Which mental truth does my Thinking Self either ignore or misunderstand?

From the point of view of the Higher Self, there is a reason for everything.

Where there's life, there's hope.

4. Which conscious decision or intention will link me with my inner guidance again?

For example: *I decide to say YES to life again and become ready to view my life situation from a new and constructive viewpoint under the guidance of my Higher Self.*

I recognise the sense and the opportunity in the current situation and what I stand to gain from it.

5. Which qualities will help me here?

Hope, trust, endurance.

6. How can I tell when my positive *Gorse* potential is growing?

For example: *I can see new, positive beginnings and positive possibilities in my life.*

Ideal
Communication

1. Experience the negative *Gorse* state as consciously as possible:

"Oh, what's the use!"

Buy the weekend edition of a daily newspaper, turn to the Economy section and cut out all the headlines that appear to be objectively reporting worrying or negative developments (not to be confused with the *Willow* exercise, p. 230), e.g. "Company X is to make 2,100 workers redundant" etc.

As you read these articles you may involuntarily ask yourself whether in fact there is still anything at all positive to look forward to in the future.

Check your perceptions and thoughts and write them down in your flowers journal.

2. Observe the *Gorse* principle around you:

Many people who have already more or less come to terms with a chronic psychological or physical problem are in the *Gorse* state: children being brought up in institutions, dialysis patients, the long-term unemployed.

Others endure *Gorse* states as a result of a chronic deficiency which they experienced at home during their upbringing and that leads them even at an early age to believe themselves shut off from the sunny side of life.

Yet the *Gorse* principle in particular is also often found in its positive form in our society: in institutions that prove through their activities that it is worthwhile maintaining hope and giving positive signals, and also in people who, for example, look after the disabled or visit prisoners on a voluntary basis.

3. Discover and develop your positive *Gorse* potential:

My **Thinking Self** must give up judging situations purely according to reason and must turn to my **Feeling Self**. It must understand that life is constantly offering new possibilities if it listens to and picks up the impulses from the Higher Self through my **Feeling Self**.

"My new opportunities – the next step in my development"

Carry out a role-play with yourself. Imagine that you are a counsellor who helps people in difficult circumstances to work out new and positive starts in life and possible ways of tackling their situation. You are at the same time both counsellor (Co) and client (Cl). Now carry on a dialogue in several steps:
Example:
As a result of an accident, a sportsman has been left with a stiff knee and can now no longer play any competitive sport.

Co: What is the situation that you need to accept?
Cl: *"I can no longer practise my profession."*

Co: What are your personal strengths? Try to count up as many as you possibly can.
Cl: *"Communication skills, a gift for teaching, skill at working with my hands ..."*

Co: Which of these skills are you still able to use?
Cl: *"Well, come to think of it, all of them."*

Co: Which of these abilities have you never deliberately used in the past?
Cl: *"Skill at working with my hands, gift for teaching."*

Co: Are you ready to take a new step in your development?
Cl: *"Yes."*

Co: Have any new opportunities already presented themselves which you have taken no notice of so far?
Cl: *"I have received various enquiries from ex-colleagues asking whether I could help them to repair their sports equipment."*

Co: What form might your next step take?
Cl: *"Phoning round and letting people know that I am considering setting up a repair service for sports equipment."*

Co: Do you have a vision for your future activity that could also serve higher interests?
Cl: *"Using the money earned from repairing sports equipment to set up a sports club for the disabled."*

The important thing for people in the *Gorse* state is to carefully register every single step in their growth, thereby showing them over and over again that a new, positive chapter in their life has already begun.

1   2   3   4   5   6   7   8   9   10   11   12

14. HEATHER
THE IDENTITY FLOWER

1. How can I tell when I am in the negative *Heather* state?

By thoughts like:
"Who cares about me now?"
"Who can I tell about this now?"

By feelings like:
Emotional hunger, inner neediness.

By reactions like:
Finding it hard to cope with being alone.
When meeting friends, hardly asking how they are but immediately telling them about yourself.
Feeling subconsciously that you are the centre of the universe that everything else hinges on.

By energy qualities like:
An energy vacuum that needs to be filled.

2. How does the disruption of communication with my inner guidance come about?

My **Feeling Self** is emotionally so undernourished that it reacts like a newborn child, completely dependent on its mother to care for it.

But the corresponding signals are transmitted not to the **Higher Self** or my **Thinking Self**, but to other **Feeling Selves** in the vicinity in order to obtain emotional sustenance and energy from them.

My **Thinking Self** thus has no chance to develop.

3. Which mental truth does my Thinking Self either ignore or misunderstand?

No system can live only on energy from outside in the long term.

We must be prepared to open up our own inner source of strength. Only this exclusive source always flows and is fed by our own Higher Self from the cosmic energy of the greater whole.

We contravene the law of our own Higher Self as well as the Law of Unity if we try to live like parasites on other people's energies.

4. Which conscious decision or intention will link me with my inner guidance again?

For example: *I decide that the time has come to grow up and take responsibility for every aspect of my life, making demands mainly on myself.*

I subordinate myself to my life plan and place trust in the help of my Higher Self to satisfy my needs.

5. Which qualities will help me here?

Courage, ability to act on my own initiative, inner consistency.

6. How can I tell when my positive *Heather* potential is growing?

For example: *I feel less wrapped up in myself and more clearly aware of the situations of people around me.*

Ideal
Communication

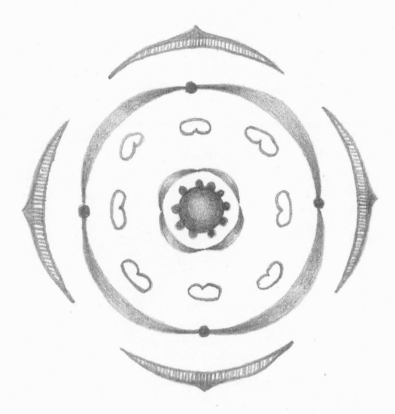

1. **Experience the negative *Heather* state as consciously as possible:**

Phone in the mirror

For this exercise you need a telephone, phone book and a comfortable seat in front of a mirror. Turn to the service pages in the phone book, listing numbers for information services such as weather forecast, consumer tips etc.

Set your timer for 15 minutes, then dial various of these talking information services, one after the other, and allow yourself to be informed. At the same time watch yourself constantly in the mirror. Notice how you respond to the different pieces of information you receive.

Watch yourself. How do you look in profile? Are you wrinkling up your forehead? Are your ears turning red ...?

Soon you will make an important discovery: the more you lose yourself in watching your reflection in the mirror, the less you will manage to grasp the actual content of the information coming down the phone line. So information is coming in all the time which you are not managing to evaluate for yourself, yet you carry on consuming it ... As you perform this exercise, observe your state of mind. How does it make you feel?

2. **Observe the *Heather* principle around you:**

The best place to observe the *Heather* principle is at a party. You will always find someone who has just met another person for the first time, manoeuvred them into a corner and is talking to them intensively, not giving them any chance to join in the conversation.

Waiting rooms and long train journeys are other situations in which people in the *Heather* state often exploit the opportunity to live out their unconscious emotional neediness. In so doing, they are totally unaware of the reactions of the person they are talking to or those sitting nearby.

3. **Discover and develop your positive *Heather* potential:**

My **Feeling Self** must be enabled to grow out of its chronic feeling of inner emptiness and to develop a differentiated, conscious awareness of its needs. Then it must learn to discover with the help of my **Thinking Self** what it can itself provide for satisfying those needs.

Before starting this exercise you should pamper your needy **Feeling Self** a little: wallow in a hot bath with your favourite bath oil, let go of all negative feelings and thoroughly enjoy …

Once you feel inwardly completely rejuvenated, sit down at a table and write the following list in your flowers journal.

My unfulfilled emotional needs

Write down at least 6 unfulfilled emotional needs and choose one of them for the following exercise.

Example: *"I would like to receive more emotional support from my partner over my problems at work."*

Then answer the following questions in relation to your situation:

- "How have I fulfilled this need until now?"

E.g.: *"I have been phoning my partner at least three times a day at the office, and spending at least another two hours discussing it with him every evening."*

- "What is the risk if I carry on like this?"
  "The risk is that my partner will switch off inside."

- "What kind of help from outside will I continue to need?"
  "Encouragement from my partner and his opinion on the behaviour and psychological reactions of my colleagues."

- "Which of the things I have been doing until now to satisfy this need could I manage without doing?"
  "The daily phone calls to the office."

- "Is there any other way in which I can satisfy my need?"
  "Yes, for example by talking to a psychologist."

Then, the most important question of all:

- "What can I do to become inwardly less dependent and to satisfy this need for myself in the future?"

You may need the help of an experienced counsellor to work out your answer to this question. The answer should run along the following lines: "The energy I turn outwards in order to coerce other people to satisfy my needs I will in future turn deliberately inwards to develop my own personality." This is a lengthy process that often needs to be accompanied by therapy.

1   2   3   4   5   6   7   8   9   10   11   12

15. HOLLY
THE HEART OPENING FLOWER

1. How can I tell when I am in the negative *Holly* state?

By thoughts like:
"That hurts me."
"It makes me furious!"
"I am afraid of being disappointed again."

By feelings like:
Hurt, extreme anger, short temper, "poisonous" mood.
Feeling inwardly raw.

By reactions like:
Easily-hurt feelings or easily offended.
Wanting to be friendly but not managing to be so.
Responding to a colleague's innocent remark with such irritation
that you fall into a bad mood.

By energy qualities like:
Energy knotting itself up, boiling and burning.

2. How does the disruption of communication with my inner guidance come about?

The strong positive feelings of my **Feeling Self** were often misunderstood, disappointed or wounded in childhood. It therefore often reacts with mistrust to impulses from the Higher Self, and when other people show their feelings it often becomes irritated, angry, even malicious.

My **Thinking Self** allows itself to be dragged along by these feelings and loses sight of its responsibilities.

3. Which mental truth does my Thinking Self either ignore or misunderstand?

Anyone seeking unity and divine love in the outside world must inevitably be disappointed. Human feelings are always imperfect and contradictory.

We can only experience divine love by opening our hearts to our Higher Self, which always guides us in accordance with the principles of divine love.

If we can achieve this, we will then experience love on our path through life. This love allows our understanding of the divine laws to grow, enables us to think more and more with our heart, and to understand other people's feelings better and better.

4. Which conscious decision or intention will link me with my inner guidance again?

For example: I decide to accept divine love direct from its source rather than continuing to seek it in the outside world. Understanding that we are all on a journey I open my heart when I am most receptive to the impulses from my Higher Self, and I follow its guidance.

5. Which qualities will help me here?

Understanding, tolerance, love.

6. How can I tell when my positive *Holly* potential is growing?

For example: *I can find in myself more goodwill towards others and approach them with greater openness because I understand their feelings better. Since learning to be more clearly aware of the divine within myself, I can also see it more easily in others.*

Ideal
Communication

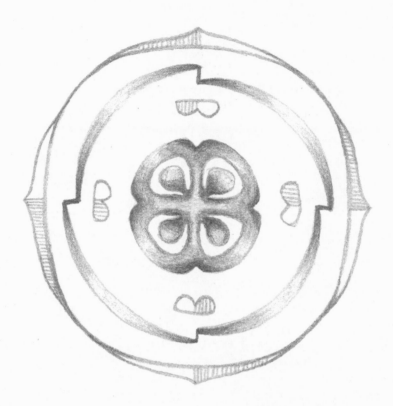

1. Experience the negative *Holly* state as consciously as possible:

"Hurt feelings"

In most cases, hurt feelings arise early on in childhood. The situation described below illustrates how this can occur.

You are four years old and, with a great deal of enthusiasm and devotion, you have gone into a meadow and picked a bunch of flowers for your mother. Your bouquet includes wild flowers, grasses, weeds – everything from the meadow that looked interesting to you. Just as you are presenting your mother with the fruit of your labours, your Aunt Anne comes into the room and says: "Goodness gracious, you've gone and picked all the weeds for miles around. Better go and chuck those on the compost heap!"

What did you feel at that instant? You probably asked yourself: "Have I done something wrong here?" You wanted to do something good, but ended up being mocked. You presumably experienced feelings such as confusion, hurt, disappointment and sadness ...

Now try to remember 5 situations in your own life in which your feelings were hurt, then write these down in your flowers journal.

2. Observe the *Holly* principle around you:

Hurt feelings occur not only in relationships between partners, but just as frequently form the unconscious basis for decisions in work situations.

For example: Two colleagues, Mr Jones

and Mr Miller, are unconsciously in competition to receive recognition from their bosses. Miller has unintentionally stolen the show from Jones. Jones is so angry with him that at the next meeting of the works committee he votes against him despite the fact that he actually shares the same opinion.

3. Discover and develop your positive *Holly* potential:

This exercise is designed to make my **Feeling Self** see that it can in no way expect the divine emotional characteristics of the Higher Self from other people. Furthermore, my **Feeling Self** needs to learn how to avoid being so easily flustered by their human – or all-too human – emotional reactions.

My **Thinking Self** needs to practise distinguishing between emotional responses to outside conditions and projecting one's personal feelings (see definition on page 29). An example of this would be found in projecting our own unconscious fear of being unable to give enough love to our partner. Then we would be afraid of receiving enough love in return.

Now continue from Exercise 1.

What hurts me?

Try to recall a situation in the fairly recent past that hurt you at the time and still hurts you now.

Example:

"My husband forgot our 13th wedding anniversary and also snubbed me."

↝ What happened?

"I had laid the table for a romantic dinner. My husband arrived home very late and as soon as he was in earshot shouted: 'Pack my case for me, will you?'"

↝ What had you expected?
"To enjoy a nice, romantic evening."

↝ What feelings did this bring up in you?
"Disappointment, frustration, mistrust."

↝ What other thoughts did you have?
"Perhaps my husband is having an affair with his secretary and is planning to take her away for the weekend."

↝ What really turned out to be the situation in the end?
"My husband had to fly to Rome unexpectedly and therefore had to stay late at the office to organise all the necessary paperwork."

↝ What patterns of behaviour did you recognise?
"Transferring the bad experiences from my parents' marriage to my own."

↝ What significance did this incident have in terms of your own partnership?
"None whatsoever, as my husband is completely different from my father."

If you couldn't find a way out of your bad mood by following through a string of questions along these lines, it could be important to talk rationally to your husband about the feeling that has been weighing upon you. In this way, the feeling can be brought back into perspective, and the heart will be able to open itself again.

1 2 3 4 5 6 7 8 9 10 11 12

16. HONEYSUCKLE
THE PAST FLOWER

1. How can I tell when I am in the negative *Honeysuckle* state?

SUPPLEMENTARY PERSONAL NOTES

By thoughts like:
"When I was still working, in sales, single, married, etc. ..."
"It's as if it happened yesterday."

By feelings like:
Melancholy, regret, homesickness, sentimental yearnings.

By reactions like:
Measuring present-day events using standards from the past, e.g.
"When I was thirty I had a fine, full head of hair, but now I've got the beginnings of a bald patch."
Being drawn as if by magic to people with whom or places where one has had positive experiences.
Finding it very difficult to sort out the past, e.g. handling your parents' flat after they die or letting go of old things.

By energy qualities like:
Heavy heart, energy flowing off behind.

2. How does the disruption of communication with my inner guidance come about?

My **Feeling Self** tries to avoid any unpleasant perceptions from the present time by clinging enthusiastically to nice memories, images and rituals.

My **Thinking Self** allows itself to be soothed by these images and to be moved to measure the present situation against inappropriate standards from the past.

As a result even the impulses from the Higher Self are not picked up correctly.

It is impossible to make a genuine choice in the here-and-now or to take responsibility for the current situation, and no learning process is able to take place.

3. Which mental truth does my Thinking Self either ignore or misunderstand?

Everything flows and is subject to continual change. The only real life is taking place now, namely at the moment between yesterday and tomorrow. The voice of the Higher Self can also only be heard in the present. By attaching ourselves to the past we distance ourselves from life, and the impulses from the Higher Self can no longer reach us.

4. Which conscious decision or intention will link me with my inner guidance again?

For example: *I decide to plunge fully into the flow of time and place trust in my inner guidance, which holds in store for me many wonderful new opportunities to develop and continue my growth.*

5. Which qualities will help me here?

Willingness to give up all fixed patterns of thinking and to view the situation from a fresh angle, being prepared to take risks, flexibility.

6. How can I tell when my positive *Honeysuckle* potential is growing?

For example: *I now see past events from a more down-to-earth and realistic viewpoint. I am coming increasingly to recognise connections with events in the present, and I feel ready to get involved with them.*

Ideal
Communication

1. Experience the negative *Honeysuckle* state as consciously as possible:

"Glorify your past"

Pick up a photo album, flick through it and allow your attention to be grabbed by a photo that represents a significant experience in your life. This may, for example, be a family occasion or a trip to the seaside with a group of close friends.

Place yourself back into that "film" as if you are in the cinema and try to re-experience the good feelings from that time. How does this make you feel? Write down your feelings in your flowers journal.

Now try to imagine that you have the power to turn back the clock. Would you like to do that? And how would you feel if you really did so?

2. Observe the *Honeysuckle* principle around you:

You probably won't have found the exercise too difficult, because the *Honeysuckle* strategy is used quite deliberately in a variety of different ways nowadays. Think about food adverts, for example, that wax lyrical about the "good, old-fashioned taste", or the many songs that recall "the good old days."

Go to a school reunion, an antiques fair or a convention of enthusiasts whose interest relates to a bygone era, and notice the way that some of the people at such events are unconsciously in tune with the zeitgeist from that period in the past. You can see this in their outward appearance and facial expressions.

It is well worth reading certain interviews and conversations with old celebrities for examples of the positive *Honeysuckle* potential. Such people are often taking stock and passing on valuable human experiences to the younger generation.

The *Honeysuckle* state often crops up in literature. Try reading the Heidi books by Johanna Spyri, for example.

You won't see any manifestation of the *Honeysuckle* principle in nature, unless perhaps you know of some animal that keeps its winter coat through the summer. Can you think of a tree that hangs on to its old leaves through to the following summer?

3. Discover and develop your positive *Honeysuckle* potential:

My **Thinking Self** must convince my **Feeling Self** that the idea of leaving "old films" behind is worthwhile and attractive, and persuade it to invest the energy that has been tied up in old pictures from the past in the present again.

My **Feeling Self** must learn to differentiate between that which is worth saving from the past and carrying with me into the present and that which – like old leaves from a tree – is better cast off in order to make space for the new.

"Take an objective look at your past"

Now continue from Exercise 1. Look again at the photograph you selected, and this time ask yourself about the negative moments that occurred at the event in question.

For example: *"Aunt Annie had a heart attack on that birthday, and nobody realised what was wrong."* Which of the feelings you experienced at that time would you prefer not to repeat?

Think about the people in the photo one by one and ask yourself how your relationship with them has developed in the intervening years. Do you have genuine mutual feelings in the present for a particular person, or have such feelings faded away?

Pick up the phone and ring one or more of the people who appear in the photograph. During the conversation take note of any old patterns of relating that both you and the other person still maintain in the present.

Supplementary recommendations

Revisit some of the places from your past. Much that you find there will now appear small and insignificant. In other things you may discover completely new dimensions.

People who are affected by *Honeysuckle* states should give some thought to the following questions at some point:

- "What problems in my present life am I avoiding by clinging to the past?"

- "Is there a situation from the past which I still grieve for, and that I could learn from now by relating to it in a completely different way?"

- "What will I gain if I decide to finally let go of something that belongs in the past?"

1   2   3   4   5   6   7   8   9   10   11   12

17. HORNBEAM
THE VITALITY FLOWER

1. How can I tell when I am in the negative *Hornbeam* state?

By thoughts like:
"Just thinking about it makes me start yawning."
"I find it a real chore."
"I can't get through this job without coffee, tea, cigarettes etc."
"That doesn't turn me on."

By feelings like:
Laziness, listlessness, lack of motivation.
No spring in your step, everything feels tedious.

By reactions like:
Wishing there were some good fairies who would deal with the work you have to get through.
Worrying that you haven't got the energy to get to the end of a task.
Everyday tasks are taxing because you carry them out half-heartedly.

By energy qualities like:
Lazy flow of energy with scarcely any wave movements.

2. How does the disruption of communication with my inner guidance come about?

For either sensible or expedient reasons, my **Thinking Self** has been operating unilaterally for quite some time in a limited framework of experience, thereby failing to take into account the needs of my **Feeling Self**.

My **Feeling Self** is frustrated, lacking in motivation, and is no longer passing on any impulses it receives from the Higher Self, in short it is not putting any energy into the game.

My **Thinking Self** tries to find stimulation in the outside world to make up for the lack of impulses.

3. Which mental truth does my Thinking Self either ignore or misunderstand?

Life is a wave-like flow in which every day is unique in its quality of time, every day takes a different shape.

Boredom or feelings that life is too routine can only arise if we restrict our own thoughts and do not give enough space to the stimulation and impulses of our **Feeling Selves**.

4. Which conscious decision or intention will link me with my inner guidance again?

For example: *I intend to let go of outdated mental patterns of expectation.*

I decide to say yes to my inner guidance from the depths of my heart and to join in fully, to allow more awareness of feelings in my life and to react more spontaneously to my feelings.

5. Which qualities will help me here?

Curiosity, willingness, attentiveness, dedication.

6. How can I tell when my positive *Hornbeam* potential is growing?

For example: *Since I have started paying more attention to my various different needs, my everyday life has been easier to cope with, and I've found more energy for it.*

Ideal
Communication

1. **Experience the negative *Hornbeam* state as consciously as possible:**

"Turn yourself into a robot!"

Set your timer for 10 minutes and pick up a telephone directory.

Start at A and turn over each page methodically, writing down the first and last name from each page on a sheet of paper.

How do you feel? Can you feel your levels of attention and motivation changing, and do you feel the way in which performing this routine, which in itself is quite straightforward, becomes more and more tedious and paralysing?

When the timer rings, stop what you have been doing and follow your first impulse, doing exactly what comes spontaneously into your mind. This will probably be something that expands your horizon again and allows a completely different side of your personality to express itself.

2. **Observe the *Hornbeam* principle around you:**

Hornbeam states can be seen wherever one-sided, repetitive and basically under-demanding activities are performed. This could be on a Monday morning in a factory, for example, or in a monotonous office job. It may also be in the home where the same activities are carried out routinely, over and over again. You can often hear people say: "The funny thing is that the less I have to do, the harder I find it to get the work done." When children are asked to do "grown-ups' jobs", they can easily fall into the *Hornbeam* state. When a five-year-old girl is made to help with peeling potatoes for a long time, she starts off by enjoying the job. But then she falls more and more silent, keeps going without any inner motivation, but cannot allow herself to stop because she wants to be "grown up." In this situation her child's needs for movement and creativity are neglected.

3. Discover and develop your positive *Hornbeam* potential:

It is important here that my **Thinking Self**, acting in its all-too sensible and down-to-earth way, should take seriously my **Feeling Self**'s need for creative self-expression and should be ready to work hand in hand with it. This is the only way for my **Thinking Self** to get back in touch with its inner guidance.

The following exercise is designed to help you to organise the necessary routine tasks in your life in such a way that your **Feeling Self** will also gain pleasure from them.

Surprise your Feeling Self with "creative routine management"

Choose a weekend to perform this exercise, and decide to carry out a specific routine task that you have been putting off for a long time. This may be, for example, clearing out the garden shed or writing long-overdue replies to that pile of correspondence.

Now think about the things you would much prefer to spend the weekend doing.

Maybe you would like to experiment with a new hairstyle or try some new household gadget.

When you now carry out the routine task you have decided on, try breaking off from time to time for the activity you enjoy, say in the following rhythm:

If the routine activity takes 2 hours, take a break after no more than 45 minutes; if it takes 6 hours, then break off at least every 100 minutes. After breaking off from the routine task, indulge in your preferred creative activity for a while.

If you dare, you can even free yourself from this structured approach to time and activity, instead juggling the two activities to and fro following your instincts. The only rule is that you should make sure that the routine task is completed by the end of the day. The fact that you have got to the end of a "boring" job enjoyably and virtually in passing will probably fill you with a sense of satisfaction.

At the end of the day make a note in your flowers journal of how you feel and what outward form your creative impulses and spontaneous activities took on. Perhaps you succeeded in discovering something in the course of this exercise that you can use again at a later date.

1 . 2 3 4 5 6 7 8 9 10 11 12

18. IMPATIENS
THE TIME FLOWER

1. How can I tell when I am in the negative *Impatiens* state?

By thoughts like:
"Pity about the time."
"We'll be finished in two ticks."
"How much longer will it take, then?"

By feelings like:
Prickling sensation inside, nervous tension, irritability.

By reactions like:
Interrupting people in mid-sentence.
Declaring things finished before they have reached fruition in order to get them out of the way.

By energy qualities like:
Energy hopping to and fro, up and down inside.

2. How does the disruption of communication with my inner guidance come about?

My **Thinking Self** has a false theoretical conception of time. It mixes up quantity with quality, and likes to purposefully pack as much as possible into as short a space of time as possible.

This has lead to my **Thinking Self** becoming disconnected from my **Feeling Self** and the Higher Self, no longer aware of their moderating and inspiring impulses.

At times my **Thinking Self** races along leaving life behind. It is not possible to fully share human experiences with others in this way.

3. Which mental truth does my Thinking Self either ignore or misunderstand?

As we are part of a greater whole, our journey through life is also entwined with the processes of life on a larger scale. Every happening has its hour. It is more important to do things as **well** as possible at the (cosmically) suitable time than to try to get them out of the way as **quickly** as possible.

4. Which conscious decision or intention will link me with my inner guidance again?

For example: *I decide to measure my time not only with a normal wristwatch, but with a watch on the inside, and to treat both myself and others more generously. Under the guidance of my Higher Self I will increasingly recognise the right moment to act or to be quiet.*

5. Which qualities will help me here?

Humility, patience, ability to empathise.

6. How can I tell when my positive *Impatiens* potential is growing?

For example: *I find myself able to wait and see how things turn out, to look on more calmly when other people are doing things more slowly than I would.*

Ideal
Communication

1. Experience the negative *Impatiens* state as consciously as possible:

"Faster and faster, more and more ..."

Try the following exercise to become more aware of the negative *Impatiens* state:

On a normal work day, set your alarm clock half an hour later than usual, jump out of bed and try to get through your normal routine as quickly as possible to make up the time: take a shower at top speed, do your hair at the same pace, bolt your breakfast down so that it doesn't touch the sides ... What is going on inside you now? Note the way you get more and more wound up, how your movements go more and more onto auto-pilot and how your mental horizons get narrower and narrower. Are you even slightly aware of your partner's mood any longer? Did you

hear what came through the radio speaker just a moment ago?

If you enjoyed this exercise, try waking up half an hour early one morning and repeat the exercise, but this time doing everything in slow motion.

2. Observe the *Impatiens* principle around you:

Go to the main railway station and stand in a position that gives you a good view over the station square. What can you see? Someone gets out of a taxi and yells at the taxi driver for being slow to produce his change. A young man leaps onto a moving bus while carrying on eating his sandwich. A businessman runs across the road whilst talking on his mobile telephone and looking at his watch, all at the same time. What unconscious mechanism is driving these people to what imaginary destinations?

3. Discover and develop your positive *Impatiens* potential:

This exercise is designed to teach my **Thinking Self** to perceive the needs of my **Feeling Self** and to develop an awareness of the relativity of our concept of time.

We all know them, those moments when time seems to stand still or when minutes seem to be endless. Time is, in reality, nothing but a means of measurement created by the Thinking Self that we, in a manner of speaking, apply to the cosmic energy flow in order to be able to mark events on the level of polarity. The time involved with experience does not pass regularly in the way that measured time passes; in other words it either "flies past" or "seems to stand still", depending on the nature of the experience. Time does not pass at all in the here and now: "When you are happy, you don't hear the clock strike the hour."

"The walk through the park"

Go to a park or other open space where you enjoy walking. Plan out a clearly-defined route of at least half a kilometre and try to cover this route in half the time it would normally take you.

While you are walking, try to take in and retain in your mind five different things, situations or objects, e.g. a bird's nest, a couple sitting on a bench, a group of children playing football etc. Write these five things down on your clipboard when you arrive at your destination.

Now retrace your steps, but take at least twice as long to cover the distance, or better still, three times as long depending on your individual temperament.

Take note this time of any additional details you can see in the five subjects you chose. For example: *"There are fledglings in the birds' nest, the parents are circling round the nest carrying twigs in their beaks. It's fun to watch them."*

When you get back to your original starting point, sit down on a bench and write down the additional things you noticed and your impressions.

You should also ask yourself the question: "What did I feel on this walk? Did I gain any inner advantage from investing extra time in the experience?"

You may be aware that you weren't really properly aware of the park at all on the first part of the walk.

Think it through: what are we actually trying to achieve, or what are we unconsciously trying to avoid, when we try to get everything done as quickly as possible? What quality of experience, contacts and opportunities for knowledge do we miss out on in the process?

1   2   3   4   5   6   7   8   9   10   11   12

19. LARCH
THE SELF-TRUST FLOWER

1. How can I tell when I am in the negative *Larch* state?

By thoughts like:
"I can't do it."
"I could never learn that."
"That's out of the question for me."

By feelings like:
Feeling of inferiority:
Feeling small, "left behind", no good.

By reactions like:
Getting into an inner panic when faced with the need to do something one lacks the confidence for.
Coming up with an excuse to avoid doing something one lacks the confidence for, e.g. "I'm not bothered about swimming."

By energy qualities like:
Low level of energy, energy current flows past.
Feeling of inner emptiness.

2. How does the disruption of communication with my inner guidance come about?

My **Feeling Self** has stored up a large number of old, devaluing and restrictive beliefs, it feels oppressed and no longer takes up new learning impulses from my Higher Self.

My **Thinking Self** adopts the same attitude instead of helping my **Feeling Self** to realise that the old beliefs no longer apply as the present circumstances are totally different.

They both unconsciously avoid any further growth process, and this makes them shrink steadily rather than grow.

3. Which mental truth does my Thinking Self either ignore or misunderstand?

Life is an ever-changing learning programme offering an endless supply of new opportunities and options. Our own, individual life plan only presents us with tasks that in some way we are able to master, and from which we are able to grow.

4. Which conscious decision or intention will link me with my inner guidance again?

For example: *I decide to stop judging my own achievements against other people's standards.*

I recognise that the challenge ahead of me is an opportunity for growth offered by my Higher Self. From now on, therefore, I will examine every opportunity thoroughly, then either accept it as it is or modify it in such a way that it contributes to my growth.

5. Which qualities will help me here?

Trust, courage, motivation.

6. How can I tell when my positive *Larch* potential is growing?

For example: *I less frequently measure myself against other people. I now tackle things that I wouldn't have dared to take on previously.*

Ideal
Communication

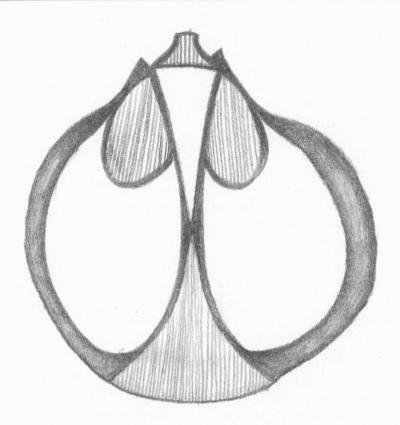

1. Experience the negative *Larch* state as consciously as possible:

What would I love to be able to do, but lack the necessary confidence?

Sit down on an uncomfortable chair in a badly-lit room, take a blunt pencil and write at least 5 answers to the question above on a piece of paper that is too small.

Choose activities that other people in similar circumstances to your own are either already involved with, or would take up without a second thought.

Example: *"I can't drive a car, and I'll never manage to learn either."*

  "What is actually stopping me?"
    "When I was of an age when learning would have been easy, I

couldn't afford the lessons, and now I've lost my nerve for driving."

  "Who is particularly good at the activity I can't manage?"
    or:

  "Who has learnt to do the very same thing just recently?"
    "My friend Paul passed his driving test on his 45th birthday."

    How helpless do you feel when you read these questions? Make a note of your impressions.

2. Observe the *Larch* principle around you:

You need to know someone quite well or watch very closely to discover the part of them that is inwardly shrinking back and not taking on any challenges whatsoever. Groups of children sometimes show the *Larch* state very clearly. The situation: they are trying out a new activity for the first time, and most children are full of enthusiasm for the exciting game, but one child is simply not joining in (not to be confused with the *Mimulus* state, in which the child is afraid of joining in).

Or again: a new type of fax machine is installed in the office. One of your colleagues says straight away: "I can't get the hang of it, I'll never work it out!"

3. Discover and develop your positive *Larch* potential:

My **Thinking Self** must encourage my **Feeling Self** to be more adventurous, not to simply accept limitations imposed by myself or others without questioning them. My **Thinking Self** must itself understand that where there's a will there's also a way.

Now continue from Exercise 1.

E.g.: *"I would like to learn to drive."*

"Stop thinking ... try doing!"

Think of something that you would very much like to be able to do, then ask yourself the following questions and make a note of your answers.

- "Who is particularly good at doing this?"

    "My friend Paul has now turned into a very good driver."

- "How does he manage to do it so well?"
  "What does he do that I don't?"

    "Paul approaches life with far less preconception than I, and does not spend his whole time comparing himself with others. When anything doesn't work out properly, he doesn't take it as personally as I do."

- "What could I do, in either just the same or a similar way, even if I am not totally convinced by it at first?"

    "I could just go and start doing it, simply give it a try."

- What is the first step I would need to take?"

    "Have a chat with Paul about it and see if he can give me a few tips for getting started."

- "Could there be any other possibilities in terms of support?"

    "I have heard that there is supposed to be a new instructional programme for use on a PC."

Now plan the next 3 realistic steps. For example:

– *Phone Paul*

– *Look in the Yellow Pages phone directory for a driving school close to where I live*

– *Make a preliminary appointment at the driving school ...*

Now continue with this train of thought and think about what you will do once you have achieved your goal:

"I'll buy a second-hand car and go to the seaside with Susan."

Write this sentence on a piece of paper, or draw a picture of the car you would like to buy, and stick it on the bathroom mirror where you can look at it every day.

1   2   3   4   5   6   7   8   9   10   11   12

20. MIMULUS
THE BRAVERY FLOWER

1. How can I tell when I am in the negative *Mimulus* state?

By thoughts like:
"Is there really no other way?"
"If only I had this behind me!"

By feelings like:
Shyness, fear, exaggerated caution, despair, nervousness.

By reactions like:
Putting off many of the things that need to be dealt with because they represent hurdles to be cleared.
Feeling happy to find someone else to accompany one on tasks like buying a pair of shoes or having a discussion with the nursery teacher rather than having to face them alone.

By energy qualities like:
Delicate quality of energy, timid, hesitant, sensitive.

2. How does the disruption of communication with my inner guidance come about?

My **Feeling Self** has had unpleasant experiences in the "harsh outside world", and feels itself abandoned by the Higher Self.

Instead of helping my **Feeling Self** by offering consolation and objective advice, my **Thinking Self** adopts the **Feeling Self's** avoidance strategies. It suffers in sympathy, bases all its decisions on the principle of pleasure and pain, and does not achieve any development.

3. Which mental truth does my Thinking Self either ignore or misunderstand?

In the world of polarity there is light (love) and darkness (fear). Of these two powers light is the stronger.

Proof: If you open the window of a room which has a light on at night, the light streams out of the window into the darkness, yet the darkness does not come into the lit room. The process of our growth takes place in the world of polarity.

Our life plan is always structured to allow the light (awareness, love) to grow in us. We can place our trust in our inner guidance without any worry.

4. Which conscious decision or intention will link me with my inner guidance again?

For example: *I decide deep down to step into the light. I will approach with courage the obstacles on my path through life, because I can trust in the guidance of my Higher Self.*

5. Which qualities will help me here?

Courage, trust.

6. How can I tell when my positive *Mimulus* potential is growing?

For example: *I have fewer fears than before and can tackle more things without feeling afraid, hesitant or timid. I feel stronger inside and better prepared for coping with life.*

Ideal
Communication

1. Experience the negative *Mimulus* state as consciously as possible:

"What situations turn me into a scaredy-cat?"

Write down on a piece of paper a list of things and situations that make you feel scared: things that you cannot get to grips with, that you keep putting off or that you would really prefer to avoid altogether.

Don't leave out those trivial worries that might appear ridiculous: *"I always avoid walking down such-and-such street because there's a big dog that always rushes up to the fence and barks extremely loudly."*

Choose one of these situations to do some further work on:

For example:

"I get nervous about going to see a new dentist."

Now describe this fear in more detail: what is it specifically that you are afraid of in this situation?

"That he or she will hit a nerve while drilling."

What would be the worst possible outcome if that happened?

"I would suffer terrible agonies."

How do you feel now? Move straight on to Exercise 3.

2. Observe the *Mimulus* principle around you:

When children have to say hello for the first time to a person they have never met before, they often cling to their mother's hand or even hide nervously behind her.

The *Mimulus* principle is harder to spot in adults because people in the

Mimulus state dislike talking about their fears. But try looking some time at the things your relatives or other people close to you avoid doing. Does your friend always try to find an escort when he or she wants to go out? Does your cousin hate spending an evening alone at home?

3. Discover and develop your positive *Mimulus* potential:

My **Feeling Self** must learn through meaningful dialogue with my **Thinking Self** that it attaches too much importance to its feelings of fear, and that these feelings are unhealthy with respect to reality.

Both must recognise that the situations the fear relates to occur in everyone's life, that one survives these situations and emerges stronger after mastering them.

"The bravery exercise"

- "Is there anything even worse that could happen?"
  "I could faint and have to go to hospital."

- "How high would I estimate the probability of this situation really arising?"
  "0.1%."

- "How do I come to be frightened of this situation in the first place, has anything like this ever happened to me in the past?"
  "Yes, when I went to see that dentist in Albania."

- "What is the probability that it will happen again now?"
  "0.1%."

- "What would happen after the worst-possible scenario (see above) developed?"
  "I would probably be injected with something in the hospital to calm me down."

And now for a question in a completely different direction:

- "Is there anything positive that could happen at the dentist's, contrary to my fear?"
  "Everything could go much more smoothly, and I might not feel any pain whatsoever."

- "What shall I do after I've been to the dentist?"
  "I'll reward myself by buying myself that book I've been wanting to read for such a long time."

Supplementary recommendations

The problem here relates first and foremost to everyday fears. There are all kinds of different exercises, approaches and techniques for learning how to handle fears and to become braver. People who feel deeply frightened should ask a therapist about other ways of working on their fears.

The following exercise is recommended for use at home: find yourself a doll and try to imagine that it is your **Feeling Self**. Sit with the doll for several sessions and lovingly discuss your worries and how you can learn together to master them.

Many people also find it helpful to practise in advance situations they are afraid of in a "dry run." Thus, for example, before your first appointment with the new dentist you might drop into the dental surgery to begin to get used to the atmosphere there.

1 2 3 4 5 6 7 8 9 10 11 12

21. MUSTARD
THE LIGHT FLOWER

1. How can I tell when I am in the negative *Mustard* state?

By thoughts like:
"What's the point?"

By feelings like:
Melancholy, emotional "lead-weighted vest", "sinking in the mire."

By reactions like:
Mood changes from one moment to the next for no apparent reason.
Inability to get enthusiastic about anything any more.

By energy qualities like:
Stagnation; dragged down by suction.

2. How does the disruption of communication with my inner guidance come about?

Powerful, destructive, collective streams of feelings like suffering, pain and sorrow (triggered by wars or natural disasters, for example) fall in step with unconscious psychic contents. My **Feeling Self** is currently overshadowed by this streaming and is no longer aware of the impulses from the Higher Self.

My **Thinking Self** cannot offer my Feeling Self any help because it is impossible to get a handle on the situation, which cannot be controlled by the powers of reason. My **Thinking Self** is drawn into the current and suffers along with my Feeling Self.

3. Which mental truth does my Thinking Self either ignore or misunderstand?

If we unconsciously open ourselves to collective currents of feeling without being able to get in touch with the Higher Self, we fall victim to these up- and down-currents. Once this happens, we can do nothing other than wait for the wave to take us back up again.

By consciously accepting these feelings when they are present, we are contributing to the transformation of our own unconscious potentials and to the collective current of feelings.

4. Which conscious decision or intention will link me with my inner guidance again?

For example: *I decide under the guidance of my Higher Self to develop my individuality more strongly so that I am not abandoned helplessly to collective currents of feeling, but can live through the highs and lows of life more consciously and recognise some form of personal sense in them.*

5. Which qualities will help me here?

Interest in the spiritual laws, attentiveness.

6. How can I tell when my positive *Mustard* potential is growing?

For example: *I experience the world of my feelings with a greater degree of differentiation and more consciously.*

Ideal
Communication

1. Experience the negative *Mustard* state as consciously as possible:

"Fallen into melancholy ..."

As the *Mustard* state arises collectively and it is hard to find an individual catalyst for it, the best way to experience this energy quality is to re-experience the ways in which great artists, poets, musicians and painters understood this state. Read literature such as *The Sorrows of Young Werther* by Goethe. Give poems the chance to move you, breathe in the *Mustard* atmosphere. For example:

A fragment from Thomas Hardy's "Hap":
"... But not so. How arrives it joy lies slain,
And why unblooms the best hope ever sown?
– Crass Casualty obstructs the sun and rain,
And dicing Time for gladness casts a moan ...

These purblind Doomsters had as readily strown
Blisses about my pilgrimage as pain."

Extract from Sylvia Plath's "Maenad" from the collection "Colossus":
"... O I am too big to go backward:
Birdmilk is feathers,
The bean leaves are dumb as hands

This month if fit for little
The dead ripen in the grapeleaves,
A red tongue is among us.
Mother, keep out of my barnyard,
I am becoming another.

Dog-head, devourer:
Feed me the berries of dark.
The lids won't shut. Time
Unwinds from the great umbilicus of the sun
In endless glitter.

I must swallow it all.

Lady, who are these others in the moon's vat –
Sleepdrunk, their limbs at odds?
In this light the blood is black.

> Listen to music by Slavonic and Nordic
> composers, such as Rachmaninov's liturgy
> or the *Valse triste* by Sibelius. Immerse
> yourself in paintings that emanate this
> deep sadness.
>
> Now decide whether you want to go
> even further and immerse yourself in the
> never-ending suffering caused by war, the
> damage and destruction caused to the
> natural world. All the different things that
> give our planet cause to mourn are
> experienced in individuals as *Mustard* states.

2. Observe the *Mustard* principle around you:

> "Collective *Mustard* clouds" hang over
> places that have experienced a great deal
> of sadness and collective suffering, or
> places where deep wounds of destruction
> have been inflicted on nature.
>
> People visiting such places unconsciously
> pick up these collective feelings of sorrow
> and reflect them in their own different,
> individual ways.
>
> Many artists are, by their nature, very
> receptive to *Mustard* states. They often
> describe the way that a black cloud descends
> at the beginning of the Christmas holiday,
> which many people find oppressive, and
> the way that cloud slowly lifts again after
> the New Year.
>
> If you walk through the streets of a
> large city nowadays and look into the eyes
> of the children you see, you will probably
> be horrified to see the amount of *Mustard*
> sadness there.

2. Discover and develop your positive *Mustard* potential:

This can only be achieved if the **Thinking Self**
and **Feeling Self** turn to the Higher Self.

My **Thinking Self** must recognise the
fact that collective feelings of pain exist
which the individual has not brought into
being consciously but must nevertheless
accept, help to carry, and respond to with
an individual reaction.

Here, too, a first step towards
consciously working on the state is to
develop an inner watchfulness, observing
exactly and possibly even writing down
precisely when a *Mustard* state takes hold,
and when it subsides again.

Mustard states will often result when a
change takes place on a higher cyclic level,
when one phase takes its leave in order to
make way for another.

This process can easily be seen in nature:
in spring, for example, when winter gives
way to summer; in autumn, when summer
gives way to winter again; at dusk, when
the day gives way to the night; in a woman
just before her menstrual period, when one
cycle ends and a new one begins.

In the *Mustard* state we can experience
the way in which, after a great collective
out-breath, breathing is stilled completely
for a moment before the new breath pours
in from the cosmos, leading us back out of
the dark into the light.

When you find yourself in the Mustard
state, try practising this or similar breathing
exercises.

Meditate ...

... on these words from Thomas Buckle:
*"Those that don't know darkness will
never seek out the light."*

1   2   3   4   5   6   7   8   9   10   11   12

22. OAK
THE ENDURANCE FLOWER

1. How can I tell when I am in the negative *Oak* state?

By thoughts like:
"I can keep going."
"Giving up is out of the question."

By feelings like:
Despondency, powerlessness, feeling as if one is walking under a yoke, having to pull a heavy waggon without any assistance from others.

By reactions like:
Not letting oneself rest until a problem is solved.
Feeling unhappy if you have to disappoint the expectations of others.

By energy qualities like:
Stiff, linear energy.
The feeling of continuing to squeeze when everything has already been squeezed out.

2. How does the disruption of communication with my inner guidance come about?

My **Thinking Self** has unilaterally over-exerted its will-power with the best of intentions and from a feeling of duty. In so doing it has inconsiderately suppressed the needs of my **Feeling Self**. My **Feeling Self** is therefore now refusing to co-operate and is no longer responding in anything other than an automatic way.

Another consequence of this is that my **Thinking Self** has cut itself off from the energy sources of the Higher Self and is only carrying on by using up more and more of its vital personal reserves of energy.

3. Which mental truth does my Thinking Self either ignore or misunderstand?

It is, of course, right to fulfil one's duties in life and to keep one's promises to other people.

However, the most important obligation is to the Higher Self in the decision to fulfil one's own, individual life plan.

If we place complete trust in our inner guidance and develop all the different aspects of our nature equally, we will succeed in fulfilling our obligations more easily and more pleasurably.

4. Which conscious decision or intention will link me with my inner guidance again?

For example: *I make the fundamental decision to work together with my Higher Self and to incorporate all the impulses that come from within me in my decisions about actions. In this way I will find it easier to fulfil my duties.*

5. Which qualities will help me here?

Insight, modesty.

6. How can I tell when my positive *Oak* potential is growing?

For example: *I am no longer viewing life with such an attitude of grim determination.*
I no longer place myself under so much pressure.
I am more creative in shaping my life.

Ideal
Communication

1. Experience the negative *Oak* state as consciously as possible:

"Obligate yourself!"

Commit yourself to completing a specific, considerable amount of work in the space of 4 hours either in your own garden or a friend's garden; e.g. mowing an 800 square-metre lawn, weeding 4 large flower beds, and not stopping before you have finished. Even if it starts raining in the meantime or someone else turns up and offers to lend a hand, don't allow yourself to be diverted from your goal, just keep going on your own.

Take careful note of the point at which the enjoyment in this work stops and after which you are only carrying on working out of a sense of obligation. Feel the natural tiring process beginning to creep in, and take note also of what is going on in your mind during this process, and what physical reactions are produced at the same time. Notice the way the gulf between mind and body becomes steadily wider ...

Write down your impressions in your flowers journal.

2. Observe the *Oak* principle around you:

Did you know that old oaks are often completely hollow inside while they still look completely undamaged outside, in other words that they maintain their facade for as long as possible?

People find themselves in the *Oak* state when they have made a promise to someone else, then find that circumstances prevent them from keeping their promise yet are unable to admit this to themselves and retract the offer. For example: a specific set of timescales has been agreed within a project team. One member of the group falls ill, which brings the project to a halt. It would be possible to look into the possibility of extending the deadline, but for the project leader it is a matter of honour – even if it involves many hours of unpaid overtime – to stick to the agreed deadline. You can see the same thing in your circle of friends and acquaintances. Which of them show a tendency to carry on with a job in the way agreed even if simpler or more pleasant ways of doing it have come to light in the meantime?

3. **Discover and develop your positive *Oak* potential:**

My **Thinking Self** must learn to attend more closely to the needs of my **Feeling Self** and to respect the natural cycles which even the body is subject to. My **Thinking Self** must be prepared to relinquish false belief systems on the subject of fulfilment of duties.

"Experience the difference"

Now turn back to page 151 and modify the *Impatiens* exercise as follows:
Starting off at a brisk pace, walk down an interesting shopping street in your neighbourhood.
Then walk back again at a leisurely pace: allow yourself to be drawn to various different shop window displays, chat to anyone you know that you meet

on the way, and finish up by settling down in a café to enjoy your favourite drink.
Now take stock of which walk left you more mentally and physically tired, and which you found more invigorating.

Supplementary recommendations

To deal with particularly stubborn *Oak* states, try answering any of the following questions that are relevant to the situation:

- "What do I still want to achieve today, come what may?"
  "I want to finish writing this chapter today."

- "What sacrifices will I have to make (in terms of time, sleep, private life) in order to achieve this result?"
  "I will have to sacrifice one hour of my night's sleep."

- "What is the worst thing that could happen if I were to postpone completion until tomorrow?"
  "I could find it impossible to meet my deadline."

- "Could there be any advantage to be gained from postponing completion until tomorrow?"
  "I may feel rather more alert tomorrow, and could perhaps have one or two new ideas."
  So, if your **Feeling Self** signals "Stop", you should persuade your Thinking Self to decide that the time has really come to stop.

1   2   3   4   5   6   7   8   9   10   11   12

23. OLIVE
THE REGENERATION FLOWER

1. How can I tell when I am in the negative *Olive* state?

SUPPLEMENTARY
PERSONAL NOTES

By thoughts like:
"It's all too much for me."
"Why can't you all just leave me in peace?"

By feelings like:
Exhaustion to the point of feeling unable to move.

By reactions like:
Feeling too tired to get undressed and go to bed at night.
Not even having the strength left to open a letter from a close friend.

By energy qualities like:
Static quality, emptiness.

2. How does the disruption of communication with my inner guidance come about?

My **Feeling Self** acts with a child-like *joie de vivre*, it wants to achieve great things and does not accept any limitations. It soon becomes completely spent through this approach to life. This also leads to a loss of sensitivity towards its own nature and needs, and the link with the cosmic energy source through the Higher Self is interrupted.

My **Thinking Self** remains unaware of this and joins in without thinking instead of intervening as a regulator with understanding and will-power. This leaves far too little energy available for learning processes.

3. **Which mental truth does my Thinking Self either ignore or misunderstand?**

The stock of vital energy is limited on the human level.

When we accept guidance by the Higher Self we are linked to the inexhaustible field of cosmic energy.

4. **Which conscious decision or intention will link me with my inner guidance again?**

For example: *I know that my personal forces are limited and that my body needs to maintain a certain reserve of strength in order to fulfil my life plan. As a result I decide to follow my inner guidance from now on. My inner guidance allows me to recognise ways of utilising my personal strengths economically, and when I need to respect my personal limits.*

5. **Which qualities will help me here?**

Humility, attentiveness, moderation.

6. **How can I tell when my positive *Olive* potential is growing?**

For example: *I recognise my bodily limits. I manage my energies more consciously and feel more inner strength.*

Ideal
Communication

1. **Experience the negative *Olive* state as consciously as possible:**

"Squander your energy"

Get yourself into the *Olive* state by indulging to excess, both physically and emotionally, in an activity you enjoy – without, of course, forgetting your bodily constitution. The activity might be reading, writing, operating a computer, making something with your hands, playing tennis, dancing, cycling, skipping or anything else along these lines. Carry on doing it until you are completely exhausted, and with your last ounce of strength make a note on your clipboard of the time it took.

Now take a few minutes or more to recover from your exertions – as long as it takes to feel fit enough again to carry on. You should also make a note of the recovery time.

Repeat this process at least three times altogether. Are you noticing that the activity phases are becoming shorter from one time to the next, and that the recovery phases need to get longer from one time to the next?

2. **Observe the *Olive* principle around you:**

You are certain to be able to recall a situation like this: You are sitting on a train when, literally at the moment the train is leaving, the door bursts open and a fellow traveller falls into a seat, coughing and out-of-breath. For several minutes his face reflects the physical as well as the mental exhaustion.

Look at the way children overestimate their powers when, full of enthusiasm, they try to help the grown-ups with the gardening. That evening they are so dog-tired that they virtually need to be carried to bed.

3. Discover and develop your positive *Olive* potential:

My **Thinking Self** needs to teach my **Feeling Self** how to stop squandering energy like a child and develop its own personal energy awareness. Both my **Thinking Self** and my **Feeling Self** must learn to co-operate closely enough to ensure that there are sufficient reserves of strength available for all the necessary tasks.

"Your energy balance sheet"

Try analysing your personal energy situation in the way that a business consultant analyses a company's finances. This will enable you to ascertain how you are currently handling your energy. With this aim in mind, answer the following questions in your flowers journal:

- "What do I use my personal energy for?"
  Look at the different categories below, calculate percentages and note them down. After entering a percentage on a line, cover it with a blank piece of paper to prevent it from affecting the other entries.

- I use about ... % of my energy on my family and my partner.

- For my career ... %.

- For further education and personal development ... %.

- For leisure and relaxation ... %.

- For domestic activities ... %.

  Now remove the blank sheet of paper and add all the percentages together.
  Are you, too, one of those people who have expended more than 100% of their energy?
  Now perform an analysis:

- "What do I use up too much energy on, although I could achieve the same result with a smaller expenditure?"

- "What should I invest extra energy in?"

- "Do I have any reserves for unforeseen circumstances?"
  Try to work out how you need to redistribute your expenditure of energy in order to avoid using up more than 100%.
  This basic exercise can be embellished as much as you like – you may, for example, like to analyse some or all of the following aspects:

- "What is the shape of my personal energy curve from morning till evening: when is my most productive time, and when do I hit a low-point?"

- "Where are my main sources of energy when I want to replenish my store: e.g. in nature, meditation, playing with my children, creative activity, light housework etc.?"
  Finally, try to get a better and better feel for the answers to these questions:

- "Which are the situations in which I expend my personal energy?"

- "When did I have the feeling that energy flowed to me from a higher source?"
  This usually occurs when we do something that is relevant to the higher plan of creation.

1   2   3   4   5   6   7   8   9   10   11   12

24. PINE
THE SELF-ACCEPTANCE FLOWER

1. How can I tell when I am in the negative *Pine* state?

By thoughts like:
"It's my fault that ..."

By feelings like:
Depression, despondency.
The feeling that one only earns the right to exist by having some-thing particular to offer.

By reactions like:
Feeling guilty if you have to make a justified demand, e.g. if someone else is sitting in your reserved seat on a train.
Finding it difficult to accept gifts.

By energy qualities like:
Energy level has dropped.
Heavy, dark.

2. How does the disruption of communication with my inner guidance come about?

My **Feeling Self** has many memories stored up that convey to it a feeling of being unwanted, bad or guilty. Despite this, it would like to be accepted and tries to achieve this through self-sacrificing actions.

Instead of helping my **Feeling Self** to clear up these misunderstandings, my **Thinking Self** reinforces them even further by orienting itself according to an exaggerated code of conduct and morals. When my **Thinking Self** is unable to live up to these standards (which is well-nigh impossible), it puts itself down, thus providing my **Feeling Self** with new reasons to carry on feeling guilty.

A great deal of life energy is wasted in this way, and I don't move any closer to my inner guidance.

3. Which mental truth does my Thinking Self either ignore or misunderstand?

The only way in which we can commit a sin is by deliberately not fulfilling our own life plan and deliberately flying in the face of the Law of Unity (see page 27).

We are responsible only for ourselves, not for other people's behaviour, and in no way can we be held responsible for every "step backwards" in development worldwide.

4. Which conscious decision or intention will link me with my inner guidance again?

For example: *I decide to grant myself the unconditional right to exist from now on, leaving all the ifs and buts behind. I accept myself warts and all.*
I know my value and give only what I can.

5. Which qualities will help me here?

Self-confidence, accepting responsibility for myself.
Ability to differentiate.

6. How can I tell when my positive *Pine* potential is growing?

For example: *If someone reproaches me for something I have done, I no longer instantly castigate myself emotionally but am able to realistically check the extent to which the reproach falls within my area of responsibility, and, if appropriate, to counter it. I now find myself enjoying life more than before.*

Ideal
Communication

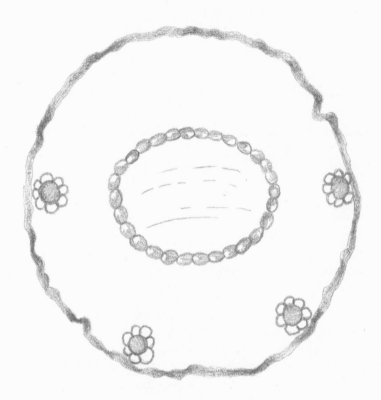

1. Experience the negative *Pine* state as consciously as possible:

"Turn yourself into a scapegoat"

Take on the role of scapegoat for a whole day. Find 3 situations in which you can quite justifiably make a particular demand, then start apologising as you deliver the demand.

For example: In a cafe you are given a dirty glass. Apologise to the waiter for asking for a clean one. If a checkout assistant short-changes you, apologise for the fact that you didn't have the right money. Record your 3 "Apology situations" in your flowers journal.

Take note of your own feelings and also particularly of the reactions of those around you when you apologise. Did the other person refute your protestations of guilt? Or did they unconsciously exploit the situation to discharge their own sense of frustration by going along with your apologies, perhaps even giving you an accusing look? If so, did this take you even deeper into your feeling of worthlessness?

Note down these observations too.

2. Observe the *Pine* principle around you:

Try noticing which of the people around you are always unconsciously coming out with apologetic phrases, devaluing themselves in the process. For example: "Excuse me, it's only me, Mrs Smith" (subconscious attitude: "Forgive me for being born"). People with strong subconscious ideas of guilt will fail to refute or contradict even the most ridiculous accusations. Such people also find it hard to accept praise or recognition as they don't accept themselves.

Note the emotional difference between an apology offered as a normal social gesture and one which is an expression of subconscious feelings of guilt.

3. Discover and develop your positive *Pine* potential:

My **Feeling Self** must learn to accept itself and my **Thinking Self** must provide moral support for this task. Both must recognise where their true responsibilities lie, to what extent they can be held to task at all, and where they should draw the line against false moral claims or other people's projections.

Recognising and accepting the reality of their own Higher Self is a life-long learning process for people with a highly-developed sense of guilt. Perform the two stages of the writing exercise below three times in alternation.

"Sweep away false guilt feelings"

- Stage 1: "I have good reason to congratulate myself."

    Recall a situation in which someone praised you.

- "What was this praise given to me for?"

    E.g. *"For a suggestion for improvement I came up with at work."*

- "How did I earn this praise?"

    "My suggestion was really good."

Record this praise in writing in your flowers journal and reinforce it with a positive symbol, e.g. ♥.

- Stage 2: "Why do I feel guilty?"

    You should now write down any feelings of guilt you are aware of, even if they seem out of proportion, and therefore are not of any particular consequence.

- "I feel guilty because ..." e.g. *"... my partner sometimes gives me such a funny look when he helps me carry heavy things upstairs."*

- Which area of responsibility does this situation belong in?

    "His, because we have an agreement that he will do the heavy jobs around the house."

- So who is responsible for this task?

    "He is."

- Have I got any reason to carry on feeling guilty about this issue?

    "No."

    If you now still find that you are experiencing feelings of guilt, look for another similar situation and work through the same exercise for that.

    Carry on repeating this exercise, at least once or twice a week, and notice any progress you make. Finally, write down any guilt feelings that you have overcome on a piece of paper, tear it up into tiny pieces and destroy them.

1 2 3 4 5 6 7 8 9 10 11 12

25. RED CHESTNUT
THE CUTTING FREE FLOWER

1. How can I tell when I am in the negative *Red-Chestnut* state?

By thoughts like:
"I know what you're thinking now."
"I can't settle down to work properly until my daughter has phoned."

By feelings like:
Feeling you are living for another person and have to experience their feelings with them.
Being unaware of your own fears, but instead making the other person's problems your own.

By reactions like:
Worrying that something unpleasant has befallen a particular person every time the telephone rings.
Worrying more about your child's runny nose than your own flu.

By energy qualities like:
Being tied long-term and unable to break free.

2. How does the disruption of communication with my inner guidance come about?

My **Feeling Self** has lost sight of itself and can only experience itself through the feelings and thoughts of another person.

As a result, my **Thinking Self** also lacks in real self-awareness and has a greatly distorted awareness of others. It translates the fears of my **Feeling Self** into concrete images that all centre on the other person.

At the same time my **Thinking Self** takes on the unconscious reactions of the other person through my **Feeling Self** and makes re-mixed images from these. Thus, as time passes it becomes more and more difficult to differentiate mentally between "mine and yours." I become ever more closely entwined with another person, and find it increasingly difficult to turn to the Higher Self.

3. **Which mental truth does my Thinking Self either ignore or misunderstand?**

Each of us is responsible for our own life plan. If we interfere with other people's life plans – and they with ours – either consciously or unconsciously, this represents an intrusion into the other's personality and thus also an infringement of the Law of Unity.

4. **Which conscious decision or intention will link me with my inner guidance again?**

For example: *I decide to retract my emotional feelers to within appropriate limits. I intend learning to be aware of my own feelings and fears, and directing my energies into my own development.*

5. **Which qualities will help me here?**

Ability to differentiate.

6. **How can I tell when my positive *Red-Chestnut* potential is growing?**

For example: *I am becoming more and more consciously aware of my thoughts and feelings. I respect the limits of my own personality and those of others.*

Ideal
Communication

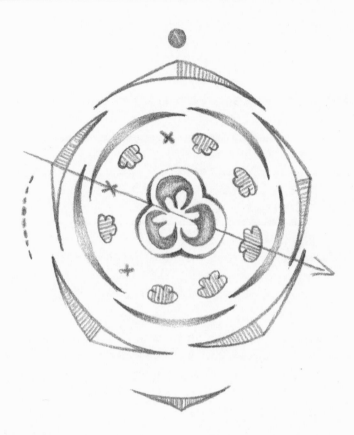

1. Experience the negative *Red-Chestnut* state as consciously as possible:

"Double life"

You will need about 3 hours to carry out the following exercise.

Imagine either a child or an adult who is dear to you, and whom you need to look after. In the course of the next two hours, keep this person, X, tied into your thoughts in everything you do. If you are making a coffee, ask yourself whether X might like one too. If you are making an arrangement by telephone, ask yourself whether it will be OK to leave X on their own for that length of time etc. When you read the newspaper, ask yourself how X would react to each particular news item.

Then, in the last half hour, write down all the fears you have in connection with X, all the terrible things that could happen to that person, e.g.: *"She might fall over and get hurt in the playground"* or *"She might catch an infectious disease."* Note down at least 7 such concrete fears in your flowers journal.

Experience the way in which your own inner freedom of movement becomes more and more restricted as you project your feelings so strongly, and the way that in your thoughts you feel increasingly tied.

2. Observe the *Red-Chestnut* principle around you:

On a metaphysical level the *Red-Chestnut* state represents the desire to melt and become one with the divine being. On the worldly level it is the state of paradise at the beginning of life when as an infant you are still joined symbiotically to your mother.

As human beings we must first liberate ourselves from both of these states in order to find our way back to this unity in a different form by developing our awareness.

Maybe you, too, know a mother who is still suckling her two-year-old son. Of course on some level she only wants the best for her child – but what might she also be avoiding by doing this?

When children grow older and learn to be aware of themselves and to mentally distinguish between themselves and the world around them, they often project their feelings onto a particular cuddly toy. If their Mum then carelessly casts the teddy aside while clearing, up they then feel that they themselves have been disregarded.

On the level of the **Feeling Self**, a child will always remain a child for its parents. On the level of the **Thinking Self**, the parents learn to value and respect the child as a grown-up person.

Look around you and note which families have succeeded in taking this step, and in which ones the relationship with their children is still based on emotional dependency.

3. Discover and develop your positive *Red-Chestnut* potential:

My **Feeling Self** must learn to be aware of my own feelings.

My **Thinking Self** must help it to distinguish which feelings are my own, which are picked up from other people and which are unconsciously projected onto others.

My **Thinking Self** and **Feeling Self** must resolve to turn to my Higher Self rather than to other people.

"I am me and you are you"

Set up two chairs facing one another and set your timer for 30 minutes. One of the chairs is for you and the other for a fictitious person about whom you are concerned.

First sit down on one chair and formulate your fear out loud. Then change your position, sit down on the second chair and make an appropriate reply. This exercise is designed to clarify where the borders need to be drawn from each side. For example:

🔑 Chair 1: "I worry about you and about whether you're doing the right thing in that situation with your landlord."
Chair 2: "I am an adult and quite capable of making my own mind up."

🔑 Chair 1: "I worry that you eat too much fat."
Chair 2: "I've also tried various different diets but have reached different conclusions from you. I've decided to carry on eating butter."

Continue this exercise by expressing a few more fears and finish off each section of this exercise by saying the following formula out loud:
"I am me and you are you.
We each have our own separate life to lead."

1   2   3   4   5   6   7   8   9   10   11   12

26. ROCK ROSE
THE LIBERATION FLOWER

1. How can I tell when I am in the negative *Rock-Rose* state?

By thoughts like:
"That can't possibly be true."

By feelings like:
Inner panic, horror.

By reactions like:
Becoming disoriented in unexpected situations and reacting by losing your head.

By energy qualities like:
Nerve system all haywire and every cell in the body getting agitated.

2. How does the disruption of communication with my inner guidance come about?

My **Feeling Self** feels under extreme threat and fears for its life.

Instead of asking my **Thinking Self** for help or turning to my Higher Self, it is paralysed with panic at the moment of terror.

In this way the **Thinking Self** cannot participate and is unable to analyse the situation and act accordingly.

3. **Which mental truth does my Thinking Self either ignore or misunderstand?**

If we are no longer able to keep a situation in perspective, the solution lies on a higher level. Only if we switch over and enter fully into the situation can unimagined powers flow to us from this higher level.

4. **Which conscious decision or intention will link me with my inner guidance again?**

For example: *I deliberately call up my Higher Self in incomprehensible situations and put myself unreservedly in the hands of its inner guidance.*

5. **Which qualities will help me here?**

Presence of mind, trust, dedication.

6. **How can I tell when my positive *Rock-Rose* potential is growing?**

For example: *In difficult situations I manage to hold my nerve better and to react with greater presence of mind.*

Ideal
Communication

1. Experience the negative *Rock-Rose* state as consciously as possible:

"The moment of terror"

Close your eyes. Imagine or remember a situation in which you suddenly got into a blind panic. You might be sitting in the cinema when it suddenly occurs to you that you have left a candle burning in the living room. Or you are sitting in a restaurant, and when the time comes to settle the bill you find that your handbag has disappeared. Or, as the train pulls out you discover that you've boarded the wrong one ...

We all know these terrible moments when it is as if we have been struck by lightning and we get into a blind panic.

Now open your eyes again and actively bring yourself back into the present: knock three times loudly on the table, stand up and stamp three times on the floor, or shout out loud.

Now see if you can reconstruct exactly how the situation passed off at the time. Where did your energy rush to at the first instant? How did your breathing respond? How did your heart feel, what was going on in your stomach? ... And so on. How many seconds would you estimate passed by until you felt completely yourself again?

Write down these observations in the form of a brief report in your flowers journal.

2. Observe the *Rock-Rose* principle around you:

Rock-Rose experiences unfortunately occur fairly frequently nowadays. Who can say that they have never experienced a near-accident: perhaps when a deer runs across the motorway when we are driving at night? You just have time to hit the brakes at the last moment. It takes a long time before you are able to get the deer's staring, panic-stricken eyes out of your mind.

Then think about the way children wake screaming from a nightmare because, as they emerge from a different world, they cannot orient themselves in reality.

Try watching real-life TV and note the situations in which people cannot understand what is going on. That moment in which the world they have been aware of up to that point collapses, and they have not yet been able to start reorienting themselves, brings out the *Rock-Rose* state.

The positive *Rock-Rose* potential is embodied by all the so-called heroes of the day who succeed in bringing off unexpected and almost superhuman achievements in such situations.

3. **Discover and develop your positive *Rock-Rose* potential:**

In the *Rock-Rose* state my **Thinking Self** and **Feeling Self** have a tendency to become paralysed.

My **Feeling Self** must learn to handle unfamiliar situations, to accept them in a flash and to open itself immediately and unreservedly toward the Higher Self.

Once the energy flows back again, my **Thinking Self** can also switch itself back

on again. For this, along with inner willingness, above all good nerves will be required.

Strengthen your nerves and sharpen your presence of mind

All the "first-aid measures" we know – from clapping, shouting and stamping to taking *Rescue* remedy – ultimately have as their aim the reorientation of our consciousness in our physical body. Consciously adopt one or more measures in your personal "self-help repertoire." The only decisive factor is breaking through the mental autopilot and firmly diverting attention in a different direction, namely towards the Higher Self.

Courses in many spiritual movements can train you in different ways of handling energy changes in a flexible way. T'ai chi and yoga are just two examples of this approach.

Diet, as is well known, can also play a large part in strengthening the nerves. You should eat foods that are rich in vitamins and nutrients, while avoiding stimulants.

Many people who have a tendency towards *Rock-Rose* states have recognised this connection long ago and now control their diet accordingly. More detailed information on diets to strengthen the nerve system can be found in publications advising on such matters and in healthfood shops.

27. ROCK WATER
THE FLEXIBILITY FLOWER

1. How can I tell when I am in the negative *Rock-Water* state?

By thoughts like:
"You need to be firm with yourself."
"From nothing comes nothing."
"It's a matter of principle."

By feelings like:
Joylessness, self-restriction.
Hardness, untouchability.

By reactions like:
Not tolerating any exceptions to a rule you have set yourself.
Seeing your "trip" through to the bitter end, even when the going gets really tough.

By energy qualities like:
Rigid "straitjacket" of energy.

2. How does the disruption of communication with my inner guidance come about?

My **Thinking Self** has misunderstood the Higher Self's idea of striving for perfection and wants – in keeping with its limited material understanding – to force a development by applying dogma.

In this process the impulses from my **Feeling Self** are renounced and deliberately suppressed by my **Thinking Self**.

My Higher Self is incapable of making its presence felt.

SUPPLEMENTARY
PERSONAL NOTES

3. Which mental truth does my Thinking Self either ignore or misunderstand?

The ideal type of waymarkers in life are those which point us in the right direction to go but don't give us fixed standards to measure our achievements against.

Only our inner guidance enjoys complete insight into our life plan and will guide us in such a way that all aspects of our personality will develop in harmony. Life is not a competitive sport, it is a cosmic dance.

4. Which conscious decision or intention will link me with my inner guidance again?

For example: *I open myself to all the different aspects of my being and react flexibly to the waves in the flow of my life. In this way I will arrive safely at my destination.*

5. Which qualities will help me here?

Spontaneity, curiosity, adaptability, love.

6. How can I tell when my positive *Rock-Water* potential is growing?

For example: *I am better able to perceive and allow my vital needs.*

I achieve more than I used to achieve, and without "seizing up" so frequently.

I have gained a more relaxed attitude toward the people around me.

Ideal
Communication

1. Experience the negative *Rock-Water* state as consciously as possible:

"Discipline exercise: a matter of principle!"

Choose an hour in which you have only routine jobs to carry out, and set your timer for 15 minutes.

The object of the exercise is to either raise your knees alternately as far as possible towards your chin 10 times or to do 5 extremely deep knee bends every 15 minutes, in other words 4 times in the allotted hour.

No exception is allowed to this rule – regardless of whether the telephone or doorbell rings, whether you feel the urge to visit the toilet or feel the need for a drink.

When the hour is up, make yourself comfortable in an armchair and allow the feelings you experienced in the last 60 minutes to wash over you again. In particular, try to recall how many times in the course of the hour you had to suppress a spontaneous or a vital need in your body.

Make a note of your impressions in your flowers journal.

2. Observe the *Rock-Water* principle around you:

Because the *Rock-Water* state is relatively easy to recognise, it is a popular subject with cartoonists: grim-faced joggers running down the road, people who spend their lives in the gym or swimming endlessly up and down the pool ...

If you find yourself in a business

meeting, look at the way some people are barely able to remain seated. Suppressing the urge to get up and move, they force themselves to stay still, merely tapping their feet with nervous energy until, eventually, they get up after all and leave the room.

If you know someone who has dieted to lose a lot of weight in order to fit into clothes that are four sizes smaller, ask them what made them decide to do it and what sacrifices they have had to make in order to go on for years without gaining a single gram again.

3. Discover and develop your positive *Rock-Water* potential:

It is important here that your **Thinking Self** should turn to your **Feeling Self**, should recognise its needs and willingly include them in its planning. The **Thinking Self** must also learn to understand that theories, as their name implies, are "theoretical" and serve only as guide-lines, but are not the actual path.

To avoid carrying out the following exercise in too "*Rock-Water*-ish" a way, that is too strictly, if necessary you should take 2 drops of *Rock Water* in a glass of water before starting.

"Follow your spontaneous impulse"

Go to a children's playground, make yourself comfortable on a bench and, quite relaxed, watch the goings-on. At first glance it seems to be nothing but noisy mayhem.

Now watch one or two of the children for about 15 minutes and notice the way in which, in their playful way, they consistently pursue a goal without allowing this to alter their mood in any way. If you find yourself overcome by a spontaneous impulse to throw back an escaping ball, to give someone a push on a swing or join in the play in some other way, follow the impulse.

If you have time, stay where you are for another half hour and notice the pattern of energy on a higher level that is mirrored in the playground. It is like the ebb and flow of a tide – at one moment it is all excitement that seems to be rising, then for a while peace and quiet return.

Supplementary recommendations

Every month go out once "on the spur of the moment."

Arrange to meet a friend whom you think of as rather happy-go-lucky, and travel together to somewhere neither of you know well. Leave the map in the car and wander about the city spontaneously with no goal and no plan.

Start by going along with your companion's ideas. Later, if you have a spontaneous idea of your own, go along with that. That evening you will be astounded at all the things you have experienced and how refreshed you feel in body and soul!

1   2   3   4   5   6   7   8   9   10   11   12

28. SCLERANTHUS
THE BALANCE FLOWER

1. How can I tell when I am in the negative *Scleranthus* state?

By thoughts like:
"Should I or shouldn't I?"
"I feel torn."
"It has its pros and its cons."

By feelings like:
Inner volatility, uncertainty, feeling torn.

By reactions like:
Coming out of the door and dithering for ages over whether to turn left or right.

By energy qualities like:
Discord; energy jumping around all over the place.

2. How does the disruption of communication with my inner guidance come about?

Because my **Feeling Self** has stored a large number of contradictory experiences, it is constantly torn between many different impulses.

Rather than searching for its own centre, it turns to my **Thinking Self** for help. My **Thinking Self** is unable to cope with this situation because of the fact that, due to a mental error, it has no desire to organise and evaluate the impulses.

For its part, my **Thinking Self** adapts itself to the fluctuating impulses from my **Feeling Self**, leaning first towards one option, then to another.

In this way more and more energy is tied up in the outside world, one's own stability becomes more and more tenuous and the link back to the Higher Self ever more problematic.

3. Which mental truth does my Thinking Self either ignore or misunderstand?

On the metaphysical level inhabited by the Higher Self, all mental possibilities are of equal value.

However, in order that the life plan can be implemented on the polarity level they must be tested and evaluated by the **Thinking Self.**

Decisions between Yes and No, beneficial and non-beneficial need to be taken constantly.

In the long run this can only succeed if we seek the link with our Higher Self.

4. Which conscious decision or intention will link me with my inner guidance again?

For example: *I decide to consider only those possibilities that fit in with my own life plan, however many possibilities from outside may present themselves.*

To recognise these, I will trust in my inner guidance and only decide "Yes" if my "gut feeling" is also positive.

5. Which qualities will help me here?

Ability to differentiate, will-power, patience, self-discipline.

6. How can I tell when my positive *Scleranthus* potential is growing?

For example: *Despite a great many impulses, I am able to maintain my inner equilibrium and intuitively make the right decision at the right moment in time.*

Ideal
Communication

1. Experience the negative *Scleranthus* state as consciously as possible:

"The agony of choosing"

Set your timer for 20 minutes, sit down, relax, and imagine the following situation:

On your birthday, in the same post, you receive invitations from two very dear friends to two different theatre performances, both on the same evening. It is the last night of both plays.

Of course you can only accept one invitation, and you feel inwardly torn.

Now write the pros and cons of each invitation on a piece of paper.

Even after this process the two invitations still appear equally tempting: you cannot choose between them.

What state do you find yourself in when the timer rings 20 minutes later?

Make a note of these feelings in your flowers journal.

2. Observe the *Scleranthus* principle around you:

Scleranthus is concerned with the principle of balance, which manifests itself symbolically almost wherever you look. You can see it, for example, in the way the seesaw moves up and down on the children's playground, in the way the wind opens and closes a door, in the way the spectators turn their heads from side to side at a tennis match.

Observe the positive side of the *Scleranthus* principle on another level, for example in a shop: a good salesperson will present the pros and cons of two articles to the prospective buyer in a vivid manner, yet without pre-empting the customer's decision.

Go to a toy shop, buy one of those weighted dolls that always bobs back into an upright position when it is pushed over, and watch the way it always finds its way back to its centre.

It is a *Scleranthus* state manifesting itself in sea-sickness, so the advice given to sufferers from that affliction is symbolically appropriate for anyone in a *Scleranthus* state: don't look at the movement of the waves but concentrate on the more distant destination on the horizon.

3. Discover and develop your positive *Scleranthus* **potential:**

My **Thinking Self** must learn that on our level of life there are arguments for and against everything. Making a decision means making a choice, in other words rejecting one of the two possibilities. My **Thinking Self** needs to understand that we must nonetheless always make decisions, as this is the only way in which any further development can take place.

It needs to develop the will to explicitly ask my **Feeling Self** for co-operation in situations where decisions need to be taken, and then to use reason to sort its reactions into order of priority before reaching a constructive decision.

"Make a decision!"

For the following exercise ask yourself a question that you have been looking for the answer to for a long time, and write that question down in your flowers journal.

E.g.: *"Should I sell the holiday flat that we haven't used at all for the last 2 years?"*

List the pros and cons of this situation alongside one another on one page in your flowers journal.

- In favour of selling: *"It costs us several hundred pounds a year, and we get no return for all that money."*

- Against selling: *"We may never find another holiday flat in such a good position again."*

- In favour of selling: *"The prices for holiday flats may go down in the coming years."*

- Against selling: *"My daughter could take the flat over from me later on."*

- In favour of selling: *"My daughter may put down roots and stay in America."*

Once you have written down all the points you can think of, get up and go into another room, or at least sit down on a different chair.

Take a couple of deep breaths, centre yourself, and allow the decision to arise within you.

- My decision is: *"I will sell the holiday flat."*

Confirm this decision by setting it down in black and white in your flowers journal.

Finally, answer the following question:

- *"What is the first step towards implementing this decision that I will take right now?"*

"Writing the 'for sale advertisement'"

*... so, **just do it!***

1   2   3   4   5   6   7   8   9   10   11   12

29. STAR OF BETHLEHEM
THE COMFORT FLOWER

1. How can I tell when I am in the negative *Star-of-Bethlehem* state?

By thoughts like:
"I just don't want to go into that."
"I can't cope with it."

By feelings like:
Feeling stunned or crippled, quiet sorrow.

By reactions like:
Unexpected, aggressive recriminations hit you like a drug with a sledgehammer effect, leaving you speechless.

By energy qualities like:
Energy is withheld, reduced to a trickle, blocked up or crystallised in the system.

2. How does the disruption of communication with my inner guidance come about?

My **Feeling Self** is afraid of being overwhelmed by negative impulses as a result of experiences that shocked it in the past. It keeps out all further impressions by sealing itself off on all sides, while maintaining itself in a kind of twilight state. The link with the Higher Self is disrupted.

It is difficult for my **Thinking Self** in this state to contact, help and console my **Feeling Self**, and my **Thinking Self** has no choice but to stay passive.

3. Which mental truth does my Thinking Self either ignore or misunderstand?

Everything that comes to us in life is a part of our life plan and provides us with opportunities to develop.

We are never subjected by our inner guidance to a load that is too heavy for us to cope with.

4. Which conscious decision or intention will link me with my inner guidance again?

For example: *I resolve to open myself to new impressions and experiences. If I am affected by an event that I had neither foreseen nor wanted to occur, I will open myself to my inner guidance as soon as possible and exploit the dynamic element of what has happened to gather new insights.*

5. Which qualities will help me here?

Willingness, courage, trust.

6. How can I tell when my positive *Star-of-Bethlehem* potential is growing?

For example: *I allow more things to affect me, but do not let myself become overwhelmed.*

I am better able to cope with unexpected events, and can process them more realistically.

Ideal
Communication

1. Experience the negative *Star-of-Bethlehem* state as consciously as possible:

"Ice-cold hand"

It is easy to familiarise yourself with the *Star-of-Bethlehem* state if you understand it symbolically on the physical level. For this exercise you need a small bucket containing ice-cold water. Before starting the exercise, take a look at the clock and note what time it is.

Now plunge your left hand into the ice-cold water and hold it in there until it feels lifeless or numb.

Then draw your hand slowly out of the water and "feel whether or not you can feel anything at all." Your hand will presumably be pretty much devoid of feeling from the shock of the cold …

Now try carefully to bring your hand back to life by starting to move the fingers slowly to and fro, then clench and unclench your fist slowly several times. Keep on doing this until you can no longer feel any difference between your two hands.

Note how long it took. The time will vary from person to person, in just the same way as it takes different people different lengths of time to recover from emotional shocks.

Would you want to repeat this experiment? Probably not. What kind of person readily repeats an unpleasant experience of their own free will? You are far more likely to defend yourself in advance to avoid having the same type of experience again in the future. This is how the *Star-of-Bethlehem* pattern develops on the emotional level.

2. Observe the *Star-of-Bethlehem* principle around you:

In the *Star-of-Bethlehem* state, rather like the *Rock-Rose* state, the push of energy is too much for the individual at a particular point in time.

The **Feeling Self** seeks refuge in a protective emotional attitude by placing a kind of protective layer between itself and the outside world. As a result of this, the person concerned can only respond to impulses in a muffled way.

A tendency to the *Star-of-Bethlehem* state often develops after general anaesthetic has been used in operations, when the **Thinking Self** was switched off and the **Feeling Self** exposed to many emotional impressions that it was unable to order.

We have all known situations where we have been involved in some kind of a confrontation and found ourselves tongue-tied, with the result that we were unable to grasp the implications of the situation until several hours later.

It is extremely difficult to make accident reports while the victims are still in a state of shock because of the fact that in the *Star-of-Bethlehem* state awareness and ability to react are so limited.

3. Discover and develop your positive *Star-of-Bethlehem* potential:

"Acknowledge your feelings!"

My **Feeling Self** must learn to abandon its tendency to protect itself and to open itself up to the impressions of its feelings. But that is only possible if my **Thinking Self** is also prepared to consciously engage with these emotional impressions, to order them, evaluate them and develop a set of measures for determining how close I want and need to allow feelings to come to me.

To achieve this you must first get to know your own feelings better. The exercises for *Cherry Plum* (pp. 102–3) may be of help here.

To help yourself set out of a *Star-of-Bethlehem* state we would recommend any exercise that rapidly re-centres the energy in the body, such as the *cross-crawl* exercise from kinesiology.

This is done in a standing position, then alternately bringing the right elbow down until it touches the left knee and the left elbow to the right knee, while at the same time your eyes alternately slowly rotate in both directions. You can introduce variety to this exercise by reaching behind you with the right hand to the left hand and vice versa.

Supplementary recommendation

Anything that strengthens the soul, body and nerve system is recommended for people with a tendency to *Star-of-Bethlehem* states. You should not attempt to work deeply on old, traumatic *Star-of-Bethlehem* situations without the support of a trained therapist.

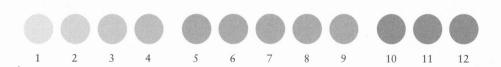

1   2   3   4   5   6   7   8   9   10   11   12

30. SWEET CHESTNUT
THE DELIVERANCE FLOWER

1. How can I tell when I am in the negative *Sweet-Chestnut* state?

By thoughts like:
"This is the end."
"Only a miracle can save me now."

By feelings like:
Fear of being unable to hold up under the weight of one's responsibilities.
Despair.

By reactions like:
All possible ways of dealing with a situation are exhausted and you feel inside that you can do nothing more.
Feeling one has reached one's absolute limit and is now standing before the abyss.

By energy qualities like:
Pressure building up from all sides.
Less and less room for manoeuvre.

2. How does the disruption of communication with my inner guidance come about?

My **Feeling Self** is alarmed by events which seem to threaten my very existence.

My **Thinking Self** has tried everything within its power but has now reached the limit of its capability. Its potentials of both understanding and will are exhausted.

It has forgotten the existence of the Higher Self.

It can no longer see any way out and fears that there will be a total breakdown.

3. **Which mental truth does my Thinking Self either ignore or misunderstand?**

All developments take place in cycles, following the principle of death and rebirth. It is important in such processes to recognise the right moment to consciously hand over control to a higher aspect.

4. **Which conscious decision or intention will link me with my inner guidance again?**

For example: *I accept that I have done everything I could in this situation and now place my trust in a higher aspect for what is still to come: "Thy will be done!"*

5. **Which qualities will help me here?**

Trust in God, dedication.

6. **How can I tell when my positive *Sweet-Chestnut* potential is growing?**

For example: *I have learned that there are situations that lie beyond my level of understanding. I recognise that in similar situations I am more able to open to my inner guidance and place my full trust in it.*

Ideal
Communication

1. **Experience the negative *Sweet-Chestnut* state as consciously as possible:**

   "The crisis before the turning point"

   Can you recall a problem situation in your life in which you could no longer see any way out and in which events came to such a head that you were forced to completely re-orient yourself? Examples of such situations might be a relationship crisis leading to a decision to part company, or a crisis at your workplace following which you decided to become self-employed.

   Describe this in your flowers journal by answering the following questions:

   ✍ What was the problem situation?
   "*I was deeply in debt.*

   ✍ What were the various things you did to try and gain control over the situation?

   Here you should list everything you did to try and save the situation.
   "*I asked for a pay rise at work. I borrowed a sum of money. I …*" *etc.*

   ✍ What did you carry on doing for too long, or what did you avoid doing?
   "*For months I carried on spending too much money.*"

   ✍ Which event became the straw that finally broke the camel's back and ushered in your rethinking process?
   "*A summons from my bank.*"

   ✍ How did you feel at that moment?
   "*In total despair.*"

   ✍ What decision did you arrive at after this?
   "*To cancel the trip to Canada I had booked long ago in order to pay off debts with the money saved.*"

How did you feel at that point in time?
   "Relieved."

What surprising development or chance happening turned up for you after you reached your decision?
   "A friend invited me to join her in her holiday cottage."

What development was only made possible through this crisis?
   "I realised that I don't want to draw in my horns, and therefore that I need to work more if I want to carry on spending money freely. That's why I turned self-employed."

If you found yourself in a similar crisis situation again today, what would you differently from then?
   "React earlier."

2. Observe the *Sweet-Chestnut* principle around you:

Crisis situations that force us to finally give up long-since outgrown or restrictive behaviour patterns shape the way we are in the here and now.

Almost all structures seem to come under scrutiny (e.g. governments, social institutions). Systems fall to pieces in order to prevent further undesired developments and to enable new ways of living to be tried.

These developments always suggest themselves a long time in advance through small corresponding events. At the height of the crisis – in the *Sweet-Chestnut* state – these signs gather force because there is now already a latent attitude of expectation within you that draws apparent coincidences or inexplicable yet fitting events up from the subconscious at the same time.

If these signs are still deliberately overlooked, ridiculed or ignored, then your inner guidance needs to make itself even clearer …

3. Discover and develop your positive *Sweet-Chestnut* potential:

My **Thinking Self** and **Feeling Self** must learn to recognise when the time has come to consciously let go of the ways I have tried to solve a problem in the past, and to open themselves completely to impulses from the inner guidance.

"Seeking out the signs"

As all your available mental, spiritual and physical resources seem to have become exhausted to no avail when you are in the *Sweet-Chestnut* state, the solution presents itself unexpectedly from a different direction.

Here too, on closer inspection the inner guidance uses dramatic patterns that vary from individual to individual. For one person it will be other people who "coincidentally" convey the necessary message. Another person will discover "his" solution in being alone, walking in the country. A third person will find the answer in a newspaper article that finds its way into her hands. Some people experience these things as a genuine miracle.

Using events from your own life, check which signs are always of significance for you when you find yourself at a turning point.

1   2   3   4   5   6   7   8   9   10   11   12

31. VERVAIN
THE ENTHUSIASM FLOWER

1. How can I tell when I am in the negative *Vervain* state?

By thoughts like:
"I know exactly what she needs."
"You have to push some people to what will make them happy."
"Dripping water will wear away a stone."

By feelings like:
Over-enthusiasm, inner unrest, irritation.

By reactions like:
Getting worked up in the course of a discussion and then being unable to wind it up.
Steam-rollering other people with one's own energy without really taking account of their reactions.
When convinced by an idea, feeling an urge to
"point out the path" to others.

By energy qualities like:
Great tension throughout the body that does not even abate at night.

2. How does the disruption of communication with my inner guidance come about?

My **Thinking Self** gets involved with inspiring ideas and wants to realise them through involving other people. In so doing, it oversteps the bounds of its own personality and then loses all sense of proportion.

My **Feeling Self** is pulled along by my **Thinking Self**, energises and ardently supports its ideas and, in the process, loses its link with my Higher Self.

3. Which mental truth does my Thinking Self either ignore or misunderstand?

The responsibility of each of us is to realise our own life plan, no more and no less. This means recognising our own limits and respecting the limits of others: "Many roads lead to Rome."

4. Which conscious decision or intention will link me with my inner guidance again?

For example: *I take responsibility first and foremost for myself.*
Before getting carried away with an idea, I take a step back, throwing it open for discussion and learning from the reactions of others.

5. Which qualities will help me here?

Self-control, an observant eye, tolerance.

6. How can I tell when my positive *Vervain* potential is growing?

For example: *If I am all fired up about something, I can verbalise my enthusiasm and still take in the ideas and reactions of the people around me. I have more real contact with my fellow human beings, and find myself able to hold conversations in a more relaxed way.*

Ideal
Communication

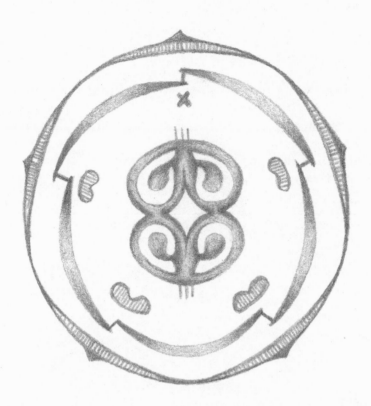

1. Experience the negative *Vervain* state as consciously as possible:

"No limits – no end!"

In the *Vervain* state we let ourselves get carried away with enthusiasm because we don't know our own limits and have lost our sense of proportion.

Do something you particularly enjoy, and do it to excess. You might, for example, listen to your favourite CD over and over again for hours on end.

Or buy 15 of your favourite fruit and eat the whole lot, one after the other, without stopping. You might keep spraying yourself with your favourite perfume until you can barely smell anything at all.

While you are doing this, see how long it takes before you reach a limit at which

you actually want to stop. Where is the point beyond which you no longer register exactly what you are doing? When does a counter-reaction come in and set a limit for you: when your own body refuses to go along with it any more – you start feeling ill – or your environment stops you as your neighbours start complaining?

In the meantime, what has become of your enthusiasm? Has it turned into a blind and uncomprehending robot driving you ever onward down the same track?

Write the answers to these questions in short sentences in your flowers journal.

2. Observe the *Vervain* principle around you:

Frank from 'Frank's Bargain Basement' exploits the *Vervain* state as a business strategy: "Not one, not two, but the whole set of three lovely plates for just one pound!" You may, for example, find highly-motivated speakers who go on and on, coming over as verging on the fanatical, at events for demonstrating new products. At the swimming pool you sometimes see enthusiastic children coming down the water slide over and over again even though their teeth have started chattering and their lips have turned blue.

You can spot the *Vervain* types at parties by the way they are lecturing other guests enthusiastically and excessively on subjects that hold no interest for them in such detail. Observe the reaction of their captive audience: can you spot a strained, polite nod of the head or a stifled yawn?

An object lesson in the positive *Vervain* state would be a conductor who is able to handle a great deal of energy with great awareness and control, setting clear limits for each section. This conductor can elicit from the orchestra the full range of nuances ranging from the most delicate pianissimo to the thundering fortissimo.

3. Discover and develop your positive *Vervain* potential:

My **Thinking Self** and **Feeling Self** must learn to recognise their limits and also be aware of the limits of other people.

By turning to the Higher Self they can develop a sense of correct proportions and grasp the smallness of the individual in relation to the Higher Intelligence.

"Many roads lead to Rome"

In order to recognise the fact that your own good idea is not the only one leading to the objective you should perform the creative exercise described below:

In your flowers journal jot down in note form 4 different diets for losing 2 kg in a weekend, for example, or 4 different approaches for organising a child's birthday party, or again 4 different ways of advertising to find new members for a club.

Did you realise that the same goal can be reached by many different routes?

Here is another little writing exercise in case you would like to train your capacity for intuitive communication:

On the left-hand side of a sheet of paper write:

✒ "I think that would do you good because ..."

Example: *"I think jogging would do you good because it stimulates the circulation."*

Then, facing what you have written, on the right-hand side of the sheet:

✒ "How might that in particular do you no good at all?"

Example: *"As you have a pretty delicate constitution, jogging may burn up too much energy in you and even make you weaker."*

Write down at least 10 recommendations and counter-arguments along these lines.

Think about the ways in which different friends would respond to the various recommendations. Finally, think through whether or not it might not be more sensible to implement these recommendations in your own life first.

1   2   3   4   5   6   7   8   9   10   11   12

32. VINE
THE AUTHORITY FLOWER

1. How can I tell when I am in the negative *Vine* state?

By thoughts like:
"Now more than ever."
"Never mind the casualties."
"No matter what the price may be."

By feelings like:
Feeling an inner compulsion to always be in the right.
Strong inner pressure.

By reactions like:
Disregarding the wishes of other people without feeling guilty about it.
Having problems with figures of authority.

By energy qualities like:
"Full speed ahead, and damn the torpedoes!"

2. How does the disruption of communication with my inner guidance come about?

My **Feeling Self** has suppressed a lot of experiences in which it was subjugated, and maintains an attitude of opposition – even towards my Higher Self.

My **Thinking Self** defines itself by how well it realises its own claims to power – its understanding and will-power serve exclusively its own ambitious interests, with complete disregard for the needs of others.

In this way it disregards the individuality of other beings and uses up their energy.

3. Which mental truth does my Thinking Self either ignore or misunderstand?

Every act committed deliberately against another person goes against the Law of Unity and automatically backfires on its perpetrator, because pressure generates counter-pressure.

Any pain we inflict on other beings we will experience sooner or later in our own body.

The urge to dominate other people will lead sooner or later to a situation in which we will ourselves be dominated by other people or circumstances.

4. Which conscious decision or intention will link me with my inner guidance again?

For example: *I acknowledge that everyone has a right to their own personality. I renounce the desire to impose my will whatever the cost.*

I decide to interact with my fellow human beings in a more co-operative way.

I obey instructions from my Higher Self.

5. Which qualities will help me here?

Humility, respect.

6. How can I tell when my positive *Vine* potential is growing?

For example: *I allow myself to think more and more with my heart and find that I can differentiate better between healthy and unhealthy ambition.*

Ideal
Communication

1. Experience the negative *Vine* state as consciously as possible:

"Impose your will!"

In the *Vine* state we want to attain our goal at any price, and without worrying about losses. The best way to experience how intense the energy gathered can become in this process is through the following experiments:

Venue: Your kitchen.

↝ Take a cardboard box and a piece of string that is only just long enough to reach round the box. Try tying the string around the box. How does the box look when you finally succeed in tying the knot? ... Has it sustained any dents or creases from the string?

↝ Now take a small can and open it using an unsuitably large can opener. What happens to the can? What is left of the can's contents?

↝ Lastly, try cramming the contents of your waste-paper basket along with a load of polystyrene offcuts into a rubbish bag that is too small. Keep trying to fit the rubbish in until the bag shows signs of bursting ...

↝ Try lighting seven candles with a single match.

How do you feel after performing "acts of force" such as these? Satisfied, triumphant, a little ashamed ...?

You should now also write an account of these episodes in your flowers journal.

2. Observe the *Vine* principle around you:

You won't have to spend long looking, because the *Vine* state imposes itself on us every day.

While you are on the way to the office in you car, someone else cuts you up and squeezes in front, in the queue at the baker's someone pushes in front of you, or you may see an argument over a parking space where neither person will give way.

How weak must people in a *Vine* state feel inside to need to present themselves so aggressively? What do they think they need to prove?

More subtle than this is the situation where the *Vine* principle expresses itself strongly in ambition – e.g. when people beaver away night and day in order to win a particular competition.

Or when they turn their *Vine* energy against themselves, e.g. by trying to halt forcibly the natural course of an illness by taking strong medicaments.

3. Discover and develop your positive *Vine* potential:

My **Thinking Self** and my **Feeling Self** must grasp the fact that all beings have an equal right to exist and that we are all performing our own task in the context of a greater plan. We should be helping rather than hindering one another in this process.

"What do I gain from going at things hammer and tongs?"

The writing exercise below is included with the aim of achieving greater flexibility in dealing with the principle of "leading and being led":

Think of a situation in your life in which you are in a position to impose your personal will by virtue of your position as a person in a position of authority or respect, yet you know that certain other people would be in disagreement with your decision. For example, you might want to organise a hill-walking expedition

as the next company outing, while most of your colleagues would prefer to go to a festival in town.

In situations like this, try working on the following questions:

- "What would I lose by giving in?"
  "Authority – people might put it down as a sign of weakness."

- "What would I gain by giving in?"
  "Good-will and a willingness on the part of my colleagues to meet me halfway."

- "What would I lose by imposing my will?"
  "My colleagues will feel that they have been steam-rollered and, in their human way, will start dragging their feet."

- "What would I gain by imposing my will?"
  "The advantage of maintaining my authority intact."

- "Which approach best serves the higher objective, in this case a good atmosphere at the workplace?"
  "Going along with the plan to go to the festival in town."

  This formula can be used in any similar situation, and you should always orient yourself to the higher objective.

Supplementary recommendation

Get the fact clear in your mind that the only way in which you can really win is by finding a solution which doesn't produce any real losers and which enables a higher goal to be achieved. In the Anglo-Saxon countries this is known as the *win/win strategy*.

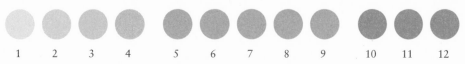

1   2   3   4   5   6   7   8   9   10   11   12

33. WALNUT
THE MIDWIFE FLOWER

1. How can I tell when I am in the negative *Walnut* state?

By thoughts like:
"If only I knew how things would turn out ..."
"I really ought to finally learn to stand on my own two feet!"

By feelings like:
Inner uncertainty, diffidence.

By reactions like:
After long consideration, taking the decision to go to the dentist for a check-up, but then allowing remarks by your partner or children to keep putting you off and preventing you from booking the appointment.

By energy qualities like:
The stream of energy gets blocked periodically.

2. How does the disruption of communication with my inner guidance come about?

My **Feeling Self** and my **Thinking Self** have reached a fundamental decision to take the next step that will carry them into a new phase of development.

But my **Thinking Self** has not yet gathered sufficient information or other people's views on the new situation and is therefore not ready to place its trust in the inner certainty of my **Feeling Self**.

My **Thinking Self** allows itself time and time again to be reduced to a state of dithering by standard objections, rational arguments or promises made in the past, and this has the knock-on effect of unsettling my **Feeling Self**. Thus both of them end up hesitating to take the decisive step to realise the change.

3. Which mental truth does my Thinking Self either ignore or misunderstand?

We attain inner fulfilment by realising our own life plan.

In order to move up the ladder of life we must first remove one foot completely from the lower rung in order to place it firmly on the next rung up.

4. Which conscious decision or intention will link me with my inner guidance again?

For example: *I decide to give my inner guidance top priority in every situation in life. Not getting flustered, I simply take the necessary steps to implement a new decision that I have recognised as right, staying true to myself through this process.*

5. Which qualities will help me here?

Inner confidence, trust, consistency.

6. How can I tell when my positive *Walnut* potential is growing?

For example: *I can grasp changes and new developments without hesitation and without allowing outside influences to make me unsure. I have gained in inner steadfastness, and my character has grown stronger.*

Ideal
Communication

1. Experience the negative *Walnut* state as consciously as possible:

"My favourite melody ... versus life's melody"

In the *Walnut* state we allow ourselves to be diverted from own path through life – you can experience this symbolically through the following exercise.

For this you will need a CD or cassette player, a CD or cassette of your favourite melody and a radio tuned to a news station.

Put the record on and dance to your favourite music, but at the same time switch on the radio news bulletin.

Notice the way the newsreader involuntarily draws your attention and how much psychic energy you need to keep your dance going well. Either while you are dancing or afterwards, situations from your life may occur to you in which the feelings were similar.

Make a few notes in your flowers journal on what you have learned.

2. Observe the *Walnut* principle around you:

It happens time and time again that pregnant women intuitively choose *Walnut* when they do not yet know on a conscious level that they are expecting a child. Fertilisation has already taken place and a mental image is beginning to take shape. But no-one yet knows exactly what the result will look like. This stage of transition brings out uncertainty, and that is where the *Walnut* principle comes into effect.

If you hear people say: "My mind is full to overflowing with the question of changing career", or "I am thinking of moving to a different city", you can recognise the *Walnut* state.

In the *Walnut* state we are further advanced on a mental level than on the level of physical manifestation – but this can also be the other way round. Then the body starts a new cycle and the mind is not yet following on behind. An example of this might be when a woman reaches the time of her menopause and does not yet recognise the associated opportunity for mental development.

Many cultures still work with the *Walnut* state in the context of rituals. Here, a step in our development is understood and manifested through a symbolic action: thus the youth turns into a man and the novice becomes a nun.

3. Discover and develop your positive *Walnut* potential:

My **Feeling Self** must orient itself more clearly to the inner guidance by the Higher Self and must stand by its inner perceptions.

My **Thinking Self** must co-operate more closely with my **Feeling Self**, must protect itself better against outside influences when turning ideas into reality and not allow itself to be confused.

"Stay true to yourself"

For this exercise you need a number of pieces of yellow and white card about the size of business cards. Imagine the situation outlined below or recall a real situation along the same lines:

You have arrived at an important decision affecting your life, such as buying a house, getting married, leaving a course of education before the end. You want to tell your relatives and friends about this decision at a birthday party. You know that some of these people will disagree with your decision and can already hear their counterarguments inside you.

Write down 7 different objections or counterarguments on 7 yellow cards.

What would you say in response to each of these people in support of your decision? Write the corresponding arguments on 7 white cards:

For example: *"I have decided to take a year of leave in order to get involved in a social project in Brazil."*

First yellow card: *"Father says: 'That will jeopardise your secure job'."*

First white card: *"There's virtually no such thing as a secure job nowadays. The important thing for my future is to develop my own abilities, and this time in Brazil will help with that."*

Second yellow card: *"Mother says: ..."*

Once you have drawn the sting from all the doubts in this manner, tear up each yellow card quite deliberately and carefully, then burn the pieces.

You should now stick the white cards in your flowers journal and, if you wish, let a drop of *Walnut* fall on this page as a symbolic emphasis.

1   2   3   4   5   6   7   8   9   10   11   12

34. WATER VIOLET
THE COMMUNICATION FLOWER

1. How can I tell when I am in the negative *Water-Violet* state?

By thoughts like:
"Nobody understands me."
"Asking others gets me nowhere."
"I prefer to stay unattached."
"I'm steering clear of that!"

By feelings like:
Feeling as if surrounded by a layer of insulation.
Feeling lonely in a crowd.
Feeling unable to make a connection.

By reactions like:
Turning down an invitation because you find it too much like hard work having to spend the whole evening talking to other people.

By energy qualities like:
Withdrawn, as if held back by an invisible hand.

2. How does the disruption of communication with my inner guidance come about?

My **Feeling Self** has overstepped its limits, lost psychic energy and would like to withdraw from the communication processes in life.

Rather than encouraging my **Feeling Self** to seek contact with my Higher Self and thus regain its equilibrium, my **Thinking Self** consolidates my **Feeling Self**'s tendency to withdraw.

It supplies my **Feeling Self** with arguments showing that there is no point in keeping up communication. In this way, no new impulses can be received and no new experiences acquired.

SUPPLEMENTARY
PERSONAL NOTES

3. **Which mental truth does my Thinking Self either ignore or misunderstand?**

Our life plan is manifested to us through other people and events. The path of the mind leads through the world, not away from it.

4. **Which conscious decision or intention will link me with my inner guidance again?**

For example: *I resolve to get fully involved with life and – where appropriate – move towards my fellow human beings in order to gain new experiences together.*

5. **Which qualities will help me here?**

Willingness to enter into new experiences, humility, tolerance.

6. **How can I tell when my positive *Water-Violet* potential is growing?**

For example: *I feel more connected with other people and find myself better able to express my feelings.*

Ideal
Communication

1. Experience the negative *Water-Violet* state as consciously as possible:

"My home is my castle"

Imagine the following situation, or recall an equivalent one: you have been invited to a party, a reception or cocktail party. You really don't feel like going to it at all.

In your flowers journal write down 5 arguments you would like to use or have used to prove that you won't miss anything by staying at home.

Example: *"I can't imagine what I could possibly gain from it – there'll be no-one there to hold a sensible conversation with – and I don't want to spend the entire evening laughing at stupid jokes"* etc.

Now add a second column alongside these notes. Admit to yourself what you are really trying to avoid by staying at home: *"I am avoiding being asked questions that are too personal – I am avoiding dancing with people who are too clumsy for my liking – I am avoiding getting into discussions and not knowing what to say – I am avoiding getting drawn into disagreements."*

Do you recognise this internal process? Your **Thinking Self** provides you with the arguments to support what your **Feeling Self** actually wants to avoid.

You can now follow this with another exercise:

Go on your own to a public festival, an open day or a flea market. Watch all the colourful goings-on, but don't talk to a soul.

Don't let anyone else start talking to you either. Be quite deliberate about avoiding making any contact, so do not buy anything.

How do you feel while you are at the event, and later on when you get home? Make a note of your feelings in your flowers journal.

2. Observe the *Water-Violet* principle around you:

Keep an eye open for the outsiders on the beach, in the gym, at the ice rink, in a meditation group, in a climbing refuge. What is it that distinguishes them from other people? Do they come over as aloof, vacant, isolated, lost in concentration ...? Observe their gestures and behaviour. Try starting a conversation with one of these "outsiders" some time. Do they respond defensively, or do you have the feeling that they are even quite grateful for the contact?

3. Discover and develop your positive *Water-Violet* potential:

My **Feeling Self** needs to understand that it doesn't have to manage everything on its own. It must learn to work out when the best thing is to set limits, and when one can and should ask for help.

My **Thinking Self** must give up its illusion of uniqueness, and both of them must forge links with the Higher Self.

"Let's communicate"

Now continue from the second part of Exercise 1.

Some time the following week go once again to a flea market or festival, and this time make positive efforts to initiate contact with other people. Enter into conversation with the kind of people that, in the normal run of things, you would never get talking to. Try negotiating or light-heartedly haggling with one of the traders.

As you do this, test your limits. See how far you can and want to go as you communicate with them – beyond just getting a good price.

Try recognising complementary behaviour patterns and character traits in the flea-market traders and the punters. Before you leave, make sure you buy at least something small to serve as a lasting reminder of this day.

Supplementary recommendation

Attach yourself to a group that is striving for a worthy goal, such as a dance group, a choir, an environmental organisation or a neighbourhood support scheme.

This should be a group of people who come together to produce a positive achievement, and in which you are dependent on mutual help and co-operation. This is because in the *Water-Violet* state you must learn to give – and also to receive.

1   2   3   4   5   6   7   8   9   10   11   12

35. WHITE CHESTNUT
THE THOUGHT FLOWER

1. How can I tell when I am in the negative *White-Chestnut* state?

By thoughts like:
"I don't want to think about that again!"

By feelings like:
Head full to bursting, overstrained, tormented.

By reactions like:
Holding inner conversations at night which go round and round in one's head.
Being unable to concentrate on the task facing one purely as a result of all the teeming thoughts.

By energy qualities like:
Spinning and vibrating inside.

2. How does the disruption of communication with my inner guidance come about?

My **Thinking Self** reacts sluggishly and has for a long time failed to take the impulses from my **Feeling Self** seriously, accept them and work on them.

As a result my **Feeling Self**'s store threatens to overflow, and it loses its natural equilibrium. The **Feeling Self** now tries at every opportunity to present the impulses that need processing to my **Thinking Self**, and through doing this it loses its link with the Higher Self.

Not until my **Thinking Self** decides to pay attention to its own task, namely ordering the impulses and making decisions, can my **Feeling Self** find its way back to its natural rhythm again.

3. Which mental truth does my Thinking Self either ignore or misunderstand?

We connect with our inner guidance through the emotional level.

For this reason we should take our emotional impulses seriously and try to deal with them promptly.

4. Which conscious decision or intention will link me with my inner guidance again?

For example: *I resolve to pay fuller attention to my impulses and make sure I deal with them as soon as they crop up.*

When I am looking for a solution to a problem I will turn deliberately to my inner guidance and ask for the necessary inspiration.

5. Which qualities will help me here?

Willingness, calmness.

6. How can I tell when my positive *White-Chestnut* potential is growing?

For example: *My head is clearer. I find that I can now wait for many of the things that I used to want to bring about through mental effort. I can now wait for a solution to surface in me of its own accord.*

Ideal
Communication

1. **Experience the negative *White-Chestnut* state as consciously as possible:**

   "A catchy tune"

   Set your timer for 15 minutes and bring yourself into the *White-Chestnut* state as follows:

   Find a record or CD with catchy music, but not your favourite music, and play it repeatedly and uninterruptedly for 15 minutes whilst humming along to the tune. Alternatively, repeat the same sentence over and over again to yourself, e.g.: "Eating and drinking keep body and soul together."

   When your timer rings, stop what you were doing and take note of your awareness and feelings. Do you feel relieved? Do the words or the tune carry on running for a while inside your head? How long for?

   Make a note of these observations in your flowers journal.

   If you cannot find a way out of this tangle of thoughts on your own, take some *White-Chestnut* in a glass of water.

2. **Observe the *White-Chestnut* principle around you:**

   The *White-Chestnut* principle is not easy to observe because the unconsciously spinning thought mechanism seldom expresses itself in words.

   In shops where music is piped all day long but there are not many customers to serve, the salespeople may well find themselves in the *White-Chestnut* state. In the intervals between serving customers their attention is not focused on any particular object, and so they are aware of the music impulses in a semi-conscious way without consciously allocating them to a particular slot.

Look at the way that such salespeople even unconsciously move in the same rhythm as the tune while they are serving customers.

3. Discover and develop your positive *White-Chestnut* potential:

My **Feeling Self** must find its way back to its natural rhythm in time through its link with the Higher Self in order not to flood my **Thinking Self** with impulses at an inopportune moment.

My **Thinking Self** must re-cultivate a willingness to consciously grasp impulses, to classify them and formulate decisions from them and ensure that those decisions are actually implemented. The link with the Higher Self has the effect of calming the stream of thoughts as there is a fundamental direction provided by the life plan.

"Spring cleaning for your thoughts"

For this exercise you should prepare a double page in your flowers journal by dividing it up into one wide column (left-hand page) and 4 narrow columns (right-hand page). Give these columns headings as follows:

Column 1: Thought
Column 2: "Deal with today"
Column 3: "Deal with this week"
Column 4: "To be dealt with later"
Column 5: "Thought rejected and
            dropped"

First retune your **Feeling Self** so that it can find its natural time rhythms again. Set your timer for 10 minutes and centre yourself, either by the method described on pages 67 to 68 or using another method with which you are familiar.

When the timer has rung, turn your mind to the question:

"What is still on the list?"

Now let the thoughts rise up from your relaxed state; these will presumably be the thoughts that need to be attended to most urgently.

In the first column in your flowers journal write down all the thoughts that surface, one below the other.

The next step is to organise these thoughts and put a cross in the appropriate column on the right for each one.

Allow one thought to surface after the other in this manner for 20 minutes.

Examples:

Thought 1: *"I should finally get round to phoning my sister in Manchester."*

Cross in column 2.

Thought 2: *"Buy some extra cutlery."*

Cross in column 5.

Thought 3: *"Plan my next summer holiday."*

Cross in column 4 – etc.

Finish this exercise by looking through your thoughts list once more with a view to fixing exact deadlines. How do you feel now?

1   2   3   4   5   6   7   8   9   10   11   12

36. WILD OAT
THE VOCATIONAL CALLING FLOWER

1. How can I tell when I am in the negative *Wild-Oat* state?

By thoughts like:
"I'm always seeking and never finding."
"That option would appeal to me too."

By feelings like:
Dissatisfaction.
Feeling unsure about one's own inner attitude.

By reactions like:
Having plenty of acquaintances but not really belonging properly in any group.
Friends say: "You dance at too many other people's weddings."

By energy qualities like:
*Energy dissipates itself in different directions
and never reaches any destination.*

2. How does the disruption of communication with my inner guidance come about?

My **Feeling Self** is under the spell of my **Thinking Self** and allows itself to be intrigued time and time again by new ideas and projects.

My **Thinking Self** acts like an adolescent; it wants to make something special happen, but is not yet prepared to take any responsibility. Instead of looking within for his specialness, my **Thinking Self** believes it can find it in the outside world. It breaks off contact with the Higher Self over and over again because it is afraid of having to pin itself down.

Thus no process of learning something is ever really seen through to the end.

3. Which mental truth does my Thinking Self either ignore or misunderstand?

Life offers an infinite number of possibilities for expression. The only way to find out which of these are compatible with our own life plan is in dialogue with our inner guidance.

To do this we need to focus less on the bustle of life around us, listening instead to what is going on within ourselves.

Anyone wishing to find inner fulfilment must be prepared to become fully involved with a task.

4. Which conscious decision or intention will link me with my inner guidance again?

For example: *For each new idea that I would like to put into practice, I ask my inner guidance to make sure that I understand clearly the extent to which this idea is compatible with my life plan. After this I can assign priorities.*

I am prepared to accept all the consequences of decisions once I have made them, and to see acts through to completion once I have started them.

5. Which qualities will help me here?

Willingness, seriousness, attentiveness.

6. How can I tell when my positive *Wild-Oat* potential is growing?

For example: *I am more purposeful and consistent in my actions and possess greater clarity concerning my goals in life.*

Ideal
Communication

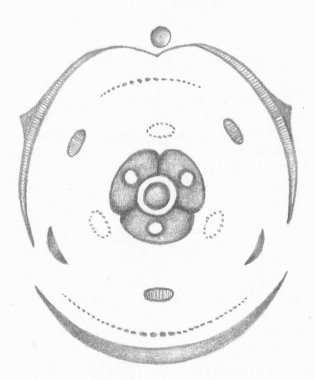

1. Experience the negative *Wild-Oat* state as consciously as possible:

"Tempting possibilities"

Imagine that you need to choose only one from a number of equally attractive possibilities, or try to recall a real situation from your life.

🔑 Example:
> You have completed a course of training to become a hotel salesperson and you now immediately receive four offers of employment:

🔑 *You can start as a trainee in a chain of hotels that is famous worldwide.*

🔑 *You can become involved in building up a hotel business from scratch in a new holiday village.*

🔑 *You can become assistant manager in the top hotel in a renowned resort in the former East Germany.*

🔑 *You can take a job in a tourist centre in Hawaii.*

> Write each of these offers on a separate sheet of paper.

In fact you are tempted by all of these possibilities. But which one tempts you most of all? You haven't really got time to carry out any proper research. What's more, there isn't the option to hold several of the offers open – you must make a decision within the next 24 hours. How do you feel when faced by this demand? Commit your feelings to paper in your flowers journal.

2. Observe the *Wild-Oat* principle around you:

The *Wild-Oat* pattern often exhibits traits associated with puberty. Try asking young people what kind of career they have in mind and take note of the "dream jobs" that come up.

Young people naturally orient themselves by the attractive external aspects of a career without realising the inner consequences.

People with pronounced *Wild-Oat* tendencies seek "something special" either in their private or working lives, but do not want to finally commit themselves because they are afraid of possibly missing something better still. Does anyone you know behave like this?

3. **Discover and develop your positive** *Wild-Oat* **potential:**

My **Feeling Self** must look for the link to the Higher Self in order to reestablish the connection with its own life rhythms and patterns.

My **Thinking Self** must be ready to test the impulses from my **Feeling Self** realistically, make decisions and stand by them.

Now continue from Exercise 1 to learn how to use *Wild-Oat* states constructively in the future.

"Find your main thread!"

Not all of us have a narrowly-defined role in life – but we all have characteristic patterns in life reflecting our life plans. People characterised by *Wild Oat* need to learn to recognise the themes relevant to their lives amongst all the different possibilities.

In *Wild-Oat* situations work on the following questions in order to find out how a particular opportunity may work to the advantage of your life plan.

🔑 "What is it about this possibility that appeals to me?"

🔑 "What is it about this possibility that doesn't appeal to me?"

🔑 "What would I gain from realising this possibility?"

Outside: e.g. *possibilities for career development, prestige, income.*

Inside: e.g. *pleasure, inner satisfaction.*

🔑 "What would I have to bring with me if I were to decide in favour of this possibility?"

Outside: e.g. *physical energy, extra time, money.*

Inside: e.g. *psychic energy, willingness to take a risk.*

🔑 "What special challenges or unusual learning opportunities could this possibility hold for me?"

🔑 "Could I imagine getting involved with this opportunity on a long-term basis?"

Now compare the different analyses with one another and notice the life patterns and inner desires that run through all the alternatives like a main thread. Try to see what it is that you are really looking for in all these possibilities.

You may, for example, realise that: *"I am looking for a task that will constantly present me with new challenges and which I can get closely involved with on a personal level."*

Find out which of the available possibilities will allow you to live out this desire most fully.

1   2   3   4   5   6   7   8   9   10   11   12

37. WILD ROSE
THE ZEST FOR LIFE FLOWER

1. How can I tell when I am in the negative *Wild-Rose* state?

By thoughts like:
"There's nothing anyone can do, that's just the way it is."
"I came to terms with this situation long ago."

By feelings like:
Indifference.
Subliminal sadness.

By reactions like:
Having mentally thrown in the towel in certain problem areas. Other people cannot understand this, as circumstances are not nearly so hopeless when viewed objectively.

By energy qualities like:
Listlessness, paralysis.

2. How does the disruption of communication with my inner guidance come about?

My **Feeling Self** mistakenly believes that it is going to die and is in the process of resigning itself to this.

Communication with my Higher Self and the **Thinking Self** is interrupted. My own life energy has stopped flowing. The result of this is that my **Thinking Self** is paralysed and is no longer capable of developing any initiative.

All developmental processes stagnate.

3. **Which mental truth does my Thinking Self either ignore or misunderstand?**

Just as in winter in the natural world, so also in our emotional life there are phases in which all external activities come to rest in order for inner reserves of strength to be replenished. We should not, however, hang on to these situations.

The Higher Self makes the decision on any withdrawal from life or a particular area of life that may or may not ultimately take place. As long as we are still alive, we bear a responsibility in life.

4. **Which conscious decision or intention will link me with my inner guidance again?**

For example: *I decide to enter into life again.*
I say "yes" to life, devoting myself to life.

5. **Which qualities will help me here?**

Willingness, interest, will-power.

6. **How can I tell when my positive *Wild-Rose* potential is growing?**

For example: *I hear myself say: "It has been a wonderful day",*
"I'm looking forward to such-and-such", "I enjoy that", or "Life
is great."

Ideal
Communication

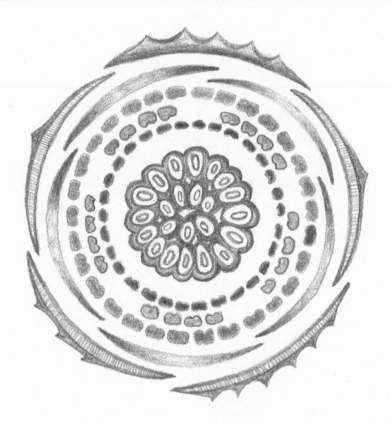

1. Experience the negative *Wild-Rose* state as consciously as possible:

"10 minutes of apathy"

For this exercise you will need your timer, a cassette recorder and a cassette of lively music.

Set the timer for 10 minutes, lie down or sit down, and recall a situation in which you felt completely drained and apathetic – e.g. by a serious illness or sitting by someone else's death bed – where you were reduced to the point where you couldn't care less about anything at all.

Try to re-experience this feeling. What thoughts come up to the surface, if any?

If you can't think of a situation like this, try wallowing in the following lines from the novel *The Outsider* by Albert Camus:

"That meant, of course, I was to die. Sooner than others, obviously. 'But,' I reminded myself, 'it's common knowledge that life isn't worth living anyhow.' And, on a wide view, I could see that it makes little difference whether one dies at the age of thirty or three-score and ten – since, in either case, other men and women will continue living, the world will go on as before. Also, whether I died now or forty years hence, this business of dying had to be got through, inevitably."

When the timer rings, jump up, switch on the cassette recorder and shake the lethargic feeling out of your body again in time to the music. If possible, round off this exercise with a short walk in nature.

2. Observe the _Wild-Rose_ principle around you:

The _Wild-Rose_ state often arises extremely early on in childhood, perhaps even during the birth process or in the course of a very serious illness when the **Feeling Self** believes it has reached the end and is now going to have to die.

An example of people in the negative _Wild-Rose_ state is provided by those unfortunates who are given psycho-drugs to keep them quiet, and you see them sitting vacantly on a park bench, apparently doing no more than vegetating. Or take a look at the dried-out plant that you left in the garage through the winter and forgot to water. Or the lifeless meadow in November when the powers of nature have withdrawn under the ground.

3. Discover and develop your positive _Wild-Rose_ potential:

For people in the _Wild-Rose_ state the most important thing is to get to the point where the **Feeling Self** regains its interest in life. Your **Feeling Self** will have to be thoroughly manoeuvred into this situation by your **Thinking Self**.

"Allow yourself to be carried away by life's infectious quality!"

Even when you don't feel suitably motivated, go on your own to places "where life is really buzzing", to a party, a beer-garden or special wine-tasting gathering, where people are squeezed together on benches, maybe even linking arms and swaying from side to side.

Go to an open-air swimming pool and watch the children on the water chute. Spend some time playing with baby animals. Enrol on a dance course, ideally folk-dancing where the dancers fire one another up and dance jubilantly. And don't miss out on going for a drink with the others at the end of the class.

Turn your ear inwards and see if you can sense any need inside yourself, however small it may be yet, and allow your **Thinking Self** to work out a plan for satisfying this need step by step.

Every day write a list in your flowers journal of the situations in which life provided you with any enjoyment, and when anything went further than that – even if at first such successes are still very modest.

Look at the principle of death and rebirth in nature. Spend your next holiday close to some water: lie down on the beach and be aware of the coming and going of the waves. Watch a river flow downstream away from you. Meditate by a waterfall.

Take on the power of the four elements in yourself. Try getting up before sunrise and experience the dawning of the day, the awakening of life all around you.

Supplementary recommendation

Pamper yourself quite deliberately, for example by having a reviving, scented bath, say a milk bath with rose oil (stir 10 drops of rose oil into a beaker of milk, then pour the mixture into your bath water).

1   2   3   4   5   6   7   8   9   10   11   12

38. WILLOW
THE DESTINY FLOWER

1. How can I tell when I am in the negative *Willow* state?

By thoughts like:
"They didn't play fair with me."
"Life is unjust."

By feelings like:
Furious impotence inside, resentment, bitterness.

By reactions like:
*Looking for and finding circumstances or other people to blame
every time anything negative happens.*
Feeling out of sorts when you see other people's happiness.

By energy qualities like:
Anger smouldering away in the belly.

**2. How does the disruption of
communication with my inner
guidance come about?**

My **Feeling Self** adopts a
challenging attitude –
even towards the
Higher Self. It sulks
if its needs are not
fulfilled, and
feels itself as a
victim of fate.

Instead of conveying an objective view of the situation to my **Feeling Self**, my **Thinking Self** allows itself to be drawn into the same attitude. It takes on the feelings of apparent powerlessness and supplies matching arguments and justifications.

3. Which mental truth does my Thinking Self either ignore or misunderstand?

The events we experience are shaped through our consciousness and our thoughts. It is therefore important that we should think constructively in terms of our Higher Self.

Life is cause **and** effect, action **and** reaction, give **and** take.

4. Which conscious decision or intention will link me with my inner guidance again?

For example: *I accept that every happening that I have anything to do with also has something to do with me, and contains a constructive learning opportunity for me.*

I am trying to recognise this straight away and to act accordingly.

5. Which qualities will help me here?

Confidence, willingness to learn, creativity.

6. How can I tell when my positive *Willow* potential is growing?

For example: *I can more and more frequently recognise the deeper contexts of an event.*

I can look at both sides of a situation and accept my part in it.

Ideal
Communication

1. Experience the negative *Willow* state as consciously as possible:

"Feeling like a victim ..."

Many people become victims of fate through no fault of their own. They may have to defend their lives in a war or may lose everything they own in a natural disaster.

Open a newspaper and mark 10 headlines that deal with this kind of subject.

In events like this that are the product of fate, the Bach flower *Willow* can be beneficial – but they are not the *Willow* state that Bach actually meant where one puts up with an uncomfortable situation without trying to change it.

Now pick up a pair of scissors and cut headlines out about people who have been turned into victims, but this time you, the

reader, ask yourself why those involved put up with the situation for so long and why they didn't make any changes sooner. Example: "Woman lived for 15 years with a violent man who beat her."

Now try to recall one or more situations in which you yourself were in the *Willow* state.

Example: The person you rent your flat from had been sick for five years and has finally died. The heirs sell the house and you blame them for taking away your home, feeling a victim.

If you cannot uncover a *Willow* memory of your own, bring to mind a situation from your circle of family or friends that you were closely involved in.

Now put this situation into perspective by comparing it with the first disaster headlines you highlighted in the newspaper.

How serious is your situation in comparison with the one in the news …?

2. Observe the *Willow* principle around you:

How do people behave when they become victims of a situation? Certain unemployed people, for example, are passive, grumble about their lot, the state or their parents who didn't get them to learn more. Meanwhile, other people afflicted by the same problem take advantage of the opportunity to retrain or try in some other way to make constructive use of this new situation in their lives.

Look at the way children angrily scold the "bad" table they have just banged into.

3. Discover and develop your positive *Willow* potential:

The *Willow* state often arises at an age in life before we have developed sufficient sense of self-responsibility, when we experience ourselves as at the mercy of the world.

Your **Feeling Self** must learn through your **Thinking Self** to keep feelings in perspective. Your **Thinking Self** must learn to recognise and make the most of its own part in every situation and, above all, its own opportunities to influence events.

Take another closer look at one of those "victim situations".

"An injustice has been done to me"

Recall a situation in which you felt yourself to be a victim and allow the feelings that this situation produced in you to come back to life in you again.

🔑 The situation:
E.g.: *"I was demoted to a less attractive job by the company I work for."*

🔑 "Whose fault was this?"
"My boss's."

🔑 "Why?"
"He thinks I am less capable than I actually am."

🔑 "In what way might I have contributed to this situation?"
"None whatsoever."
If you find that you cannot respond in any way other than defensively, go back one step through the questions. Keep doing this until a new answer presents itself, thus: "In what way might I have contributed to this situation?"
E.g.: *"I never followed up why my boss has stopped entrusting me with any new responsibilities over the last few months."*
Then carry on with the questions:

🔑 "What could I have done on my own account to change this situation?"
"I should have asked my boss earlier why he had stopped giving me any new responsibilities."

🔑 "Is there anything I could still do now?"
"If possible, request a discussion to find out the exact reasons for my demotion."

🔑 "What will I do in similar situations in the future?"
"I will pay more attention and take action earlier."

1   2   3   4   5   6   7   8   9   10   11   12

8
WHAT HAVE YOU ACHIEVED BY PERFORMING THESE EXERCISES?

8.1 THE BACH FLOWER PROFILE

You have completed a sizeable task! Focused awareness work takes a lot of energy, but that energy is invested wisely – it is quite literally the best investment you can ever make.

Now start taking stock: see what you have achieved up to this point, gain knowledge of yourself and what work you may move on to from here. For this purpose you can use the table printed overleaf, by copying the crosses over from the flower bars from the pages of exercises into this table.

The questions are set out below.

✎ **"How did I respond to the flower?"**
   1. I found it easy to grasp the principle.
   2. I found it difficult to grasp the principle.
   3. I found it impossible to grasp the principle.
   4. I would like to do further work on this principle.

✎ **"How do I assess my own relationship with this flower?"**
   5. The flower is of interest only for a current situation.
   6. The flower is of interest now and always.
   7. The flower used to be of interest, but the potential has now become positive.
   8. The flower is not of interest to me.
   9. I frequently experience this flower principle in the world around me.

✎ **"Where is the main focus for me in using this flower?"**
   10. This flower's main focus for me lies in family, relationship and partnership.
   11. This flower's main focus for me lies in career and environment.
   12. This flower's main focus for me lies in personal growth and spiritual development.

Date	Reaction to the flower					Own assessment			Main focuses for use			
	1	2	3	4	5	6	7	8	9	10	11	12
Aspen												
Heather												
Rock Rose												
Wild Rose												
Centaury												
Chicory												
Clematis												
Gentian												
Honeysuckle												
Larch												
Mimulus												
Agrimony												
Olive												
Red Chestnut												
Scleranthus												
Star of Bethlehem												
Willow												
Holly												
Beech												
Cerato												
Elm												
Gorse												
Hornbeam												
Impatiens												
Oak												
Rock Water												
Chestnut Bud												
Crab Apple												
Vervain												
Vine												
Walnut												
Cherry Plum												
Mustard												
Pine												
Sweet Chestnut												
Water Violet												
White Chestnut												
Wild Oat												

8.2 WHAT YOU CAN RECOGNISE FROM THE BACH FLOWER PROFILE

By recognising how you react to the Bach flower principles now, you are able to measure how consciously you are able to experience them.

If you found it easy to grasp the principle (cross by point 1) you have already integrated this principle well in your personality and almost certainly also experience its positive potential frequently.

    🖙 *"Which flower principles should I carry out further work on?"*
In any case on those you found hard to relate to, in other words the flowers for which you ticked points 2 or 3.

    🖙 *"Which flower principles do I experience problems with throughout my life?"*
The principles for which you have ticked point 6 evidently involve learning tasks you have brought along in your life plan. You should also do some further specific work on these.

    🖙 *"Which flower principle might be a new discovery for me?"*
Possibly those principles for which you have ticked point 9.

    🖙 *"Should I be working more at present with my Feeling Self?"*
Yes, if you have ticked an especially large number of flowers in the section of the table between *Aspen* and *Holly*.

    🖙 *"Should I be doing more for the development of my Thinking Self?"*
Yes, if you have ticked an especially large number of flowers in the section of the table between *Beech* and *Walnut*.

    🖙 *"Overall should I be making more effort to recognise spiritual principles?"*
Yes, if you have ticked an especially large number of flowers in the section of the table between *Cherry Plum* and *Wild Oat*.

    🖙 *"With which flower principles do I permit interferences with my life plan?"*
Find out these flowers for yourself.

    🖙 *"With which flower principles do I fail to respect the life plans of my fellow human beings?"*
Find out these flowers for yourself, too.

    🖙 *"With which flower principles do I go against the Law of Unity?"*
Here, too, you should enter the appropriate flowers for you personally.

    In the longer term, the following observation is interesting:

… "In which areas of life do I find myself getting into conflict time and time again with which principles?"

Thus, for example, with *Vine* in your private life, with *Centaury* in your career and so on. These observations may bring you to the starting point for personal emergency mixtures that you can prepare for the corresponding situations.

A FURTHER SUGGESTION: OBSERVE YOUR FAMILY AND THE WORLD AROUND YOU

If you are interested you can also try analysing members of your family with the help of the Bach flower profile. This may not always be easy, however, as a result of "occupational blindness." If you do this, it is interesting to follow up the answers to the following questions:

… "Which of my children, relatives, friends have the same 'chronic' flowers (point 6) as me?"

… "Which unresolved flower principle is mirrored by my family?"
E.g.: "I have problems with the Vine principle and am constantly tyrannised by my eldest daughter."

… "What themes recur time and time again in my contact with particular people?"
E.g.: "With my brother the theme of carelessness (= Clematis) crops up over and over again. Either he doesn't understand what I say or I forget immediately what he has just said. Then again, with my sister I experience the topic of Vervain. She is always trying to convince me about something or other and I cling just as firmly to an opposing idea."

By finding out shared Bach flower themes you can make a contribution to the development of awareness in your personal circle of friends – simply by working on the problem yourself and trying to see what lies behind it.

If you like try analysing a conflict in your family or circle of acquaintances as in a psychological study, but using as a basis the Bach flower principles.

Observe and notice which Bach blockages lie at which points in the process, and what positive opportunities for development for the individuals concerned are concealed in the conflict.

A broad field opens up here for working in greater depth on the Bach flower principles.

8.3 SUMMARY OF THE MOST IMPORTANT DISCOVERIES FROM YOUR BACH FLOWERS JOURNAL

The following three pages are designed for gradually gathering together the most important positive results of your work on the various flower principles to enable you to go back and access them quickly and at any time when the need arises:

1. How I experience the positive principle of the flower

2. What step in my development does this flower enable me to take?

3. My bridge to the positive potential of the flower

See also Section 6.4, pages 74 to 76.

What step in my development does this flower enable me to take?

1 Agrimony	20 Mimulus
2 Aspen	21 Mustard
3 Beech	22 Oak
4 Centaury	23 Olive
5 Cerato	24 Pine
6 Cherry Plum	25 Red Chestnut
7 Chestnut Bud	26 Rock Rose
8 Chicory	27 Rock Water
9 Clematis	28 Scleranthus
10 Crab Apple	29 Star of Bethlehem
11 Elm	30 Sweet Chestnut
12 Gentian	31 Vervain
13 Gorse	32 Vine
14 Heather	33 Walnut
15 Holly	34 Water Violet
16 Honeysuckle	35 White Chestnut
17 Hornbeam	36 Wild Oat
18 Impatiens	37 Wild Rose
19 Larch	38 Willow

Note: If you need more space set up a section in your flower diary!

My bridge to the positive potential of the flower

1	Agrimony	20	Mimulus
2	Aspen	21	Mustard
3	Beech	22	Oak
4	Centaury	23	Olive
5	Cerato	24	Pine
6	Cherry Plum	25	Red Chestnut
7	Chestnut Bud	26	Rock Rose
8	Chicory	27	Rock Water
9	Clematis	28	Scleranthus
10	Crab Apple	29	Star of Bethlehem
11	Elm	30	Sweet Chestnut
12	Gentian	31	Vervain
13	Gorse	32	Vine
14	Heather	33	Walnut
15	Holly	34	Water Violet
16	Honeysuckle	35	White Chestnut
17	Hornbeam	36	Wild Oat
18	Impatiens	37	Wild Rose
19	Larch	38	Willow

Note: If you need more space set up a section in your flower diary!

How I experience the positive principle of the flower

1	Agrimony	20	Mimulus
2	Aspen	21	Mustard
3	Beech	22	Oak
4	Centaury	23	Olive
5	Cerato	24	Pine
6	Cherry Plum	25	Red Chestnut
7	Chestnut Bud	26	Rock Rose
8	Chicory	27	Rock Water
9	Clematis	28	Scleranthus
10	Crab Apple	29	Star of Bethlehem
11	Elm	30	Sweet Chestnut
12	Gentian	31	Vervain
13	Gorse	32	Vine
14	Heather	33	Walnut
15	Holly	34	Water Violet
16	Honeysuckle	35	White Chestnut
17	Hornbeam	36	Wild Oat
18	Impatiens	37	Wild Rose
19	Larch	38	Willow

Note: If you need more space set up a section in your flower diary!

8.4 FURTHER OBSERVATIONS ON SELF-DIAGNOSIS

DIFFERENT LEVELS OF WORK INFLUENCE THE CHOICE OF FLOWERS

It has emerged that we can work with the Bach flowers for a great variety of different reasons and on different levels:

In order to harmonise turbulent emotional situations, e.g. *conflict with a partner*.

To approach longer-term themes of personal development on a psychological level, e.g. *for fear associated with decision making*.

To find help on the spiritual path in crisis situations, e.g. *where one has lost faith in the Divine Laws*.

Although in the final analysis all these levels overlap considerably, the diagnostic starting points on each level are nonetheless different and can lead to the choice of different flowers.

This is why all selection procedures or diagnostic systems have their own role within the bounds of their particular system. They always work for the person who created the system as well as for everyone else who can inwardly agree with that system, perhaps because of a similar disposition.

The more flexible such a system is and the better it can accommodate each person's individuality and the particular circumstances of the time, the more it can integrate Bach's ideal for optimum diagnosis:

"A correct understanding of the areas in which we have become cut off from our inner guidance comes from within us, through silent communication with our soul."

In the moments of spiritual confusion in which we cannot take up communication with our own soul alone, a suitable person to talk to can help, through empathy and intuition, to seek out the switch points where we have uncoupled ourselves from our inner guidance, and to find the flowers that can get the process of awareness flowing again.

In this process both counsellor and client travel part of the path together, in search of spiritual insights. This situation is very different from the phenomenon known as "helper syndrome."

"BACH FLOWER TYPES"

There is a widespread tendency amongst people who are enthusiastic about the Bach flower remedies to classify people as different "Bach flower types". This practice is counter-productive, as a particular state can become firmly entrenched in this way. Instead of saying *"You are a Vine type!"* we should go no further than saying *"The question of authority seems to be playing an important role for you at the moment."* (How can we know that the other person is not on the point of transforming this behaviour pattern for good?)

We should practise not regarding the so-called negative Bach flower states as negative in the sense of "morally reprehensible" or "bad", but as negative in the sense of "counter-productive" or "delaying the development process." When a faulty connection reveals itself in a highly complex piece of equipment, we would not normally condemn the whole thing as useless, but rather do everything in our power to get it working properly again.

DIVIDING THE BACH FLOWERS INTO GROUPS
Another point of discussion in Bach flower therapy is the tendency to divide the flowers into groups according to particular criteria.

Dr Bach's seven groups, which relate back to his seven nosodes, designate not causes but eventual states, e.g. impatience (*Impatiens*) leads to loneliness, lack of faith (*Gentian*) leads to insecurity etc.

Each Bach flower embodies a separate, unique energy quality that we can get to know step by step. Attempts to divide the flowers into groups may, at first sight, appear helpful, but experience has shown that in the long run they simply hinder the individual's process of discovery.

THE POSITIVE POTENTIALS
A point must also be made on the subject of the positive potentials: Bach recognised 38 harmonious aspects of wholeness and found 38 flowers representing these aspects.

Wholeness is, as the very word says, whole and undivided. This is why wholeness cannot be worked out through analysis, but can only be experienced individually. This explains why the positive potentials are all different in the various books written on the subject.

In place of positive potentials, this book presents "themes for learning" that are more easily manageable with the help of the appropriate flower, e.g. *Honeysuckle* throws light on the theme of *coming to terms with the past*, *Gentian* helps us get to grips with the theme of *belief*. All the themes manifest themselves in countless nuances and facets. The more we open ourselves to a theme or principle, the deeper the dimensions that can unfold.

DETERMINE YOUR LEVEL OF WORK
If you want to make the best possible use of the knowledge in this book for your self-diagnosis, you should clarify the level on which you want to work with the Bach flowers:

- intensively on the everyday emotional level

- medium-term on the psychological level on which the personality develops

- longer-term on the level of mental or spiritual development.

The Thinking Self and Feeling Self are involved to differing degrees in the diagnostic process on the various different levels.

SELF-DIAGNOSIS IN ACUTE SITUATIONS

Situations sometimes arise in which we are completely beside ourselves, unable to communicate with either the Thinking Self or the Feeling Self – they can be described graphically as "hovering by the top of the frame." In cases like this, start by taking *Rescue* in a glass of water.

At moments when your Feeling Self is a long way off-balance, you are recommended to make a spontaneous choice of flower as your initial step. As the Feeling Self possesses an innate sense or instinct for balancing energy it will spontaneously choose what can restore equilibrium at that moment in time.

At this stage people tend to use a pendulum or some other method for measuring energy. Some also draw flower cards from a pack or bottles out of the set. However, spontaneous selection is the most effective approach as it is the most direct.

At such acute moments the choice made by your Feeling Self is bound to be correct. It is sometimes also advisable to take the spontaneously-chosen flowers by the glass-of-water method, and find your way to a certain inner balance through this.

The Feeling Self cannot, however, tell on its own whether or not it is worthwhile taking this flower combination for a longer period; this it can only discover in dialogue with your Thinking Self.

The Thinking Self must recognise and decide consciously whether the spontaneously-chosen flower is a case of an acute turbulence of the soul, e.g. because of the quality of energy on that day, or a case of the tip of the iceberg in a deeper disruption to emotional equilibrium.

The greater the depth in which your Thinking Self knows the Bach flower principles, the better the chance it has of selecting the right flower.

A flower combination to be taken over a longer period should contain only those flowers that are accepted as suitable by the Thinking Self, and the acute "flowers of the day" can be taken alongside these on the same day in a glass of water.

SELF-DIAGNOSIS FOR WORK ON THE PSYCHOLOGICAL LEVEL OF THE UNFOLDING OF THE PERSONALITY OR ON THE LEVEL OF SPIRITUAL DEVELOPMENT

If you wish to work not on the acute level but on the level of the unfolding of the personality or spiritual experience, you should proceed differently.

Allow your Thinking Self and Feeling Self to hold a discussion along the following lines:

↩ *"What is my position at present?"*

↝ *"What step should I take next?"*

↝ *"Which flowers will help me to open the next door on my development path?"*

Now centre yourself by posing yourself the same questions inwardly.

Trust that the appropriate impulses from your Higher Self will be recognised intuitively by your Thinking Self and that the flowers you require will materialise in your consciousness.

Accept the answers from the flowers unreservedly and resist the temptation to "check" these messages sent by your inner guidance with the unconscious methods of your Feeling Self.

Take the flowers. See what insights they make possible for you, and turn these immediately into action.

In this way your development progresses, and your Thinking Self can take on board further impulses from your inner guidance through your Feeling Self. This makes the link between Thinking Self and Feeling Self closer and closer. The messages from the Higher Self can be received more and more quickly and be realised better and better in life.

9
WAYS OF TAKING THIS WORK FURTHER

If you have managed so far to get to know all 38 flower principles better you will find it worthwhile to carry on working continuously on your personal growth process using the Bach flowers. As you do so, you will recognise the way in which the Bach principles manifest themselves in your life, with ever-changing shades, and the way in which your personality gradually unfolds further and further like a flower.

You might take a break of around six months and then resume your work with the 38 principles. In this process you may discover how your consciousness and your perception of the 38 principles have changed, which exercises come much more easily now than before, and where you have found a way of approaching a principle on a deeper level.

But it can also happen at certain times that you feel the need to spend several weeks or even months working on a deeper level with just a small number of the flower principles.

You may even decide to take a complete break for a while from this practical work with the flower principles, in which case experience has shown that the process nevertheless continues on a subconscious level.

9.1 KEEP A REGULAR RECORD OF YOUR PROGRESS

Regardless of how you decide to work, we recommend that in any case you draw up a kind of interim balance sheet every three months, an analysis of your "Bach flower status", from which you will be able to see the direction in which your development process is moving.

So, take a second notebook and designate it as your "Bach flowers journal, volume 2." Regularly, every three months, answer a specific set of questions along the lines of those described in our example below.

If in the course of your own work on the Bach flowers you gain any insights into the principles that are of general interest, the next section of the book may be of importance to you.

Bach flower status   **Date:** ....

    ∫ "What was the general pattern in my spiritual state over the last 3 months?"

        "Very turbulent, but I held out well and often felt very well."

✿ "What changes have there been?"

"I am much better at maintaining the boundary between myself and other people. My colleagues can scarcely believe it."

✿ "Is there an area in which I have succeeded in finding a constructive way of dealing with a previous weakness?"

"Instead of just playing the part of a voiceless listener in discussions at my workplace, I now more often make a verbal contribution."

✿ "Have I discovered any new positive trait in myself?"

"I am noticeably braver than I used to be. Yesterday I jumped off the 5-metre board."

✿ "Which of the decisions I reached in the flower exercises have I carried through, and when?"

"On the 5th of September I rented a holiday cottage for a year."

✿ "To what extent has my Feeling Self become more positive?"

"I notice at an earlier stage when I am slipping back into my old pattern of feeling guilty, and I then give myself a kick on the backside."

✿ "In what respect has my Thinking Self developed?"

"I am aware that my flat is no longer in such a state of chaos and that I have become better at distinguishing the important from the unimportant."

✿ "Which Spiritual Law have I been able to get a firm handle on?"

"The law of cause and effect."

✿ "Which flower principles have I gained completely new insights into, and what are those insights?"

"With the Larch principle I have realised that life only sets me tasks that are within my capabilities."

✿ "Which flower principles have I continued to recognise as a long-term learning task for myself, and will I be doing further work on?"

"Beech and Mimulus"

✿ "What is lining itself up to form the next step in my development?"

"I must do some rethinking about my relationship with my mother."

Date for my next Bach flower status evaluation: ....
(Set down on paper now a date 3 months in the future.)

9.2 GET INVOLVED IN A RESEARCH PROJECT

"SHARING YOUR EXPERIENCE"

Anyone who opens up the positive potentials in their own consciousness will automatically be contributing to the positive transformation of collective consciousness and to the reharmonisation of our planet.

By reading this book and working on the flower principles you, too, are playing this part.

Some of you may wish to take your development further: accumulate deeper experiences, discover other forms in which the principles are expressed, and possibly find new ways of relating to them.

If you are such a person we would like to get in touch with you and encourage you to write to us.

These are the questions we are looking for answers to:

1. **In what ways do you find it helpful to have the parts of the personality personified as the Thinking Self and the Feeling Self?**

   Did the illustrations make the flower principles clearer for you?

   Would you like to work more deeply on this?

   When responding to these questions, please also send us a photocopy of your flower profile. Your name need not appear on it, but it would be useful to know your age, sex and occupation.

2. **After taking a single flower essence, can you record in written form any dreams that relate directly to the principle concerned?**

3. **Do you feel clear connections between individual Bach flower principles and gestures or sequences of movement?**

   By working on these themes within the context of our research project it could be possible to open doors to new insights that will help others later on.

   We look forward to receiving your letters.

   Please write to us under the heading "Research project", and send letters to one of the addresses shown on page 250.

The Mechthild Scheffer Institutes
for Bach Flower Therapy,
Research and Teaching
Official teaching centres for Germany, Austria and Switzerland,
approved by the Dr Edward Bach Centre, England
Information service
Seminars on Dr Bach's original flowers
Training for professional therapists
Register of therapists
Provision of consultants
Literature on the original Bach flower therapy written by Mechthild
Scheffer
Mail order service for books, working material and posters

Institut für Bach-Blütentherapie
Forschung und Lehre
Mechthild Scheffer
Lippmannstr. 57
22769 Hamburg
Germany
Telefax 040/43 52 53

Institut für Bach-Blütentherapie
Forschung und Lehre
Mechthild Scheffer
Seidengasse 32/1
1070 Vienna
Austria
Telefax 0222/526 56 51 15

Institut für Bach-Blütentherapie
Forschung und Lehre
Mechthild Scheffer
Mainaustr. 15
8034 Zurich
Switzerland
Telefax 01/382 33 19

FURTHER READING

The following books set out fundamental aspects of Dr Edward Bach's teaching.

Dr Edward Bach, **The Twelve Healers and Other Remedies**
Dr Edward Bach, **Heal Thyself**

The publications listed below are essential basic reading for anyone wishing to find out more about Bach flower therapy and the man who discovered it. These books provide the opportunity to read Edward Bach's own descriptions of all 38 flowers.

The Bach Flower Remedies Step by Step by Judy Howard *(an all-round practical guide to selecting the remedies)*
Questions and Answers by John Ramsell *(practical answers to questions concerning the remedies, their principles and practice)*
The Illustrated Handbook of the Bach Flower Remedies by Philip Chancellor *(in-depth descriptions of the 38 remedies with colour Bach flower illustrations)*
Bach Flower Remedies for Women by Judy Howard *(a journey through a woman's life and how the remedies can help the emotional difficulties encountered along the way – menstruation, pregnancy, childbirth, fertility, screening, the menopause, coping with the stresses of modern day life etc.)*
Dictionary of the Bach Flower Remedies by Tom Hyne Jones *(positive and negative aspects of each remedy)*
The Medical Discoveries of Edward Bach by Nora Weeks *(The biography of Edward Bach, written by the woman who worked most closely with Edward Bach during his lifetime and who, together with Victor Bullen, took responsibility for continuing his work after his death. This book paints a picture of Edward Bach's personal and medical development and shows how he arrived at his idea of "Healing through the Soul." The way in which the 38 flowers were discovered is described in depth.)*
The Original Writings of Edward Bach, compiled from the archives of the Bach Centre by Judy Howard and John Ramsell *(a collection of Dr Bach's letters, case notes, stories and other work, many reproduced in original script)*
Introduction to the Benefits of the Bach Flower Remedies by Jane Evans
The Bach Remedies Repertory by F.J. Wheeler
The Bach Flower Remedies Illustrations and Preparations by Nora Weeks and Victor Bullen *(The authors, Edward Bach's colleagues and close friends and later curators of the Bach Centre, describe in this book the*

production method of the Bach flower concentrates. To this day the original Bach flower concentrates are produced by the special methods for enhancing potency discovered by Edward Bach – the sun method and the boiling method. Includes colour photos of all 38 Bach flowers.)

Growing up with Bach Flower Remedies by Judy Howard *(a guide to the use of the remedies during childhood and adolescence)*

Bach Flower Remedies for Men by Stefan Ball *(written with men in mind, but it will prove invaluable to therapists, healers, lovers, wives, sisters, daughters and mothers – anyone, in fact, who has a man's welfare at heart)*

Bach Flower Remedies Workbook by Stefan Ball *(a self-contained course in the selection and use of the Bach flower remedies)*

Bach Flower Remedies for Pets by Judy Howard and Stefan Ball

All the above published by The C.W. Daniel Company Limited
Saffron Walden, Essex, UK.

The Story of Mount Vernon by Judy Howard *(an account of how Dr Bach's work has continued – a tribute to his successors Nora Weeks and Victor Bullen. Illustrated in colour)* Printed by The Bach Centre

Mechthild Scheffer, ***Bach Flower Therapy: Theory and Practice***, Munich: Hugendubel, 26th edition 1996. English edition: Thorsons, London. *(The standard work on Bach flower therapy with an extremely detailed interpretation of the 38 Bach flowers from an intellectual, psychological and practical/medical angle. This practical guide is suitable for anyone working with the Bach flowers, and has already been translated from the original German into many other languages.)*

Mechthild Scheffer, ***Original Bach Flower Therapy: Instruction book for practising doctors and healers***, Neckarsulm: Jungjohann, 5th edition 1996. English edition in preparation, Beaconsfield Publishers, Beaconsfield, UK